health
on your plate

shop & cook with Yara

by Yara Shoemaker

First edition
ISBN 978-0-9858640-0-2

Yara's Way LLC
15 Paradise Plaza, #255
Sarasota, FL 34239
Tel: (941) 480-2124
Fax: (941) 346-7469
Email: book@yarasway.com
Web: www.yarasway.com

Printed in China

Photography by Troy Plota
Design by Harriet Brewster, The Editorial Department
Editing by Doug Wagner, The Editorial Department
Page 188 image courtesy of: StockFood/Castilho

dedication and acknowledgements

This book is inspired by a love story: mine! It started with a simple Syrian girl who was passionate about healthy living for herself and the people she holds dear. When she moved to America, the girl fell in love with a very special man. She wanted a long, healthy life for both of them and that renewed her interest in wellness.

To achieve her mission of cooking real, wholesome food she researched every ingredient to strip away the colorful packaging and reveal the true nutrition contained therein. She infused cultural traditions with modern twists and compiled all her creative recipes together with essential food facts. Over time they saw improvements in their health, energy and appearance, so her husband encouraged her to share this valuable information to make positive changes in the lives of others.

For my soul mate, David: you are my love and my life. I am grateful to be alive just to know a generous and loving person like you. Thank you for all the special moments you have given me and all the incredible days ahead. You inspire me; you brought the sparkle into my life; you believe in me; you're an amazing husband and I will love you forever.

To my sister-in-law, Brittany, with whom I spent long hours, probably more than I spent with anyone else: we sat facing each other sharing the same desk, the same lunches and the same coffee pot every day for the past three years. Through all the hard work and research you were always so patient and loving. I would never be where I am without you.

To my Mama: you are the one who planted everything in me and made me who I am. You are the giver who doesn't know how to stop. You taught me the first steps for everything in life, including cooking. I remember sitting with you in the kitchen and absorbing your love and passion for food and family. I wish I could show you how much I love you, because I know that whatever I do will never be enough to thank you.

To my Papa's soul: you were my first teacher, my hero. I want just one thing: to make you proud.

To my grandmother, Tete, and her 95 years of love, hard work and giving. I see history in your eyes and stories between your wrinkles every time I look at your glowing face. You still cook the best meals in your little kitchen and with your ancient pots you could compete with any professional chef in the world.

To Yamen, Hasson and Karam: you are the three strong brothers every sister would be lucky to have. Each of you has taught me about brotherly love; you show me protection and support every single day; you are my shelter. I love all of you so much and wish you everything you dream of in life.

Thank you to everyone in my life who has taught me a lesson and all my friends who helped me along the way. I am grateful to the chefs who gave me the experience to cook with skill that complements my passion. To my readers, you are appreciated more than you know and it brings me joy to think that this book will lead you to improved health and a better life.

Contents

Important note to my readers

Throughout this book, you will find valuable health advice based on my own experience and knowledge. Therefore, any time a product or a brand name is mentioned, it is for your benefit only and not for any sponsored endorsement. All recommendations are based on published research, and I encourage everyone who reads this book to begin his or her own personal pursuit of the best health possible. Please continue to consult a medical professional about your physical health whenever necessary. I wish you a successful journey to a healthier lifestyle for yourself and those you love.

Welcome to your new healthy life!

This is not a diet book. This is simply a guidebook from one happy, healthy girl who has combined the best in traditional and contemporary nutritional wisdom to create a lifestyle that will make you thrive! This is going to be easy and you'll have fun learning my secrets to scrumptious meals that give your body a boost instead of dragging you down. My book is packed with helpful hints, and you may find yourself so excited that you want to do everything at once! That's great—I love getting people passionate about health for themselves and their families—but this advice is designed to be your fundamental first step on the path to confidence in the kitchen. Your success will come from taking one chapter at a time and mastering each section before you proudly move forward to the next stage of transformation. Before you know it, you and your loved ones will have enjoyed every challenge and arrived at revolutionary health!

Just like many of you, my chase after the optimal healthy lifestyle took me from East to West through all the major diets and cultures. My relationship with food started early, when my mama and grandmother would sit me on a stool in the kitchen and give me a simple task to help them prepare the family meal. I was delighted to spend afternoons there doing most of the talking and little of the cooking, and I absorbed much more of my family's cultural cuisine than I realized. Through culinary training with some of the top chefs in Damascus, I developed my passion for fresh Mediterranean food into a refined skill. After moving to the United States, I began putting my healthy twist on traditional dishes and made the exotic flavors fit my new nutritional goals.

Along the way, I learned the advantages and disadvantages of convenient food and mega-grocery stores. I spent a year following the macrobiotic lifestyle, feeling good but missing some of my favorite foods. Then I completed the intensely challenging Hippocrates Health Institute Life Change program, with great results but still searching for balance. After wading through seas of opinions and contradiction on subjects as diverse as wheatgrass potions and protein worship, I can feel for anyone who has ever tried and failed at a diet—too many cooks in the kitchen really do create a lot of confusion.

To sort things out, I went to the source: my grandmother. I visited her village high in the mountains to discover this vibrant 94-year-old's secret. She and the other elders of the village shared their stories and inspired me with their energy and graceful aging. Through their words, I learned much about the natural, active lifestyle that keeps them looking and feeling young.

So there's good news! All traditional diets, contemporary nutritionists and medical experts are in accord on one thing: whole grains and vegetables! They make up the main part of balanced nutrition, supplying the body with almost everything it needs. The rest of our requirements come from minimizing, not eliminating, the other food groups by preparing them in the healthiest ways. It's that simple!

With this book as your guide, you'll be armed with an arsenal of nutritional knowledge and fun, easy ways to apply it to your family's daily meals. I'll emphasize original basic recipes, inspiring variations and a few healthy tricks. Just savor the things you love and keep everything in proportion to feel sexier and look healthier. I wish you a rewarding journey to your unique lifestyle and the success that will come with it. May you read this in good health and may happiness always be yours.

FYI

Changing your lifestyle is a gradual process. Don't worry about advice that seems impossible for you to take on right now. Every little improvement makes a difference in your health, so take encouragement in the fact that you're on the right path and move on to the next section. As it gets easier for you (and it really will), you can always revisit the parts of the book that were challenging for you. Just do your best and enjoy your health!

Chapter One

the healthy kitchen

cookware

a cure in the cupboards

Why care about your cookware? Because it doesn't make any sense to purchase whole healthy foods and cook them in toxic pots and pans. While you're innocently stirring a sauce, metal and synthetic ions are sneaking first into your meal and then into your bloodstream, causing a host of health problems like cancer and Alzheimer's disease.

Pots and baking dishes

Clever cooks use enamel or glass because they are both nonreactive, long-lasting materials. High-quality brands Le Creuset and Chantal are stylishly designed and have strong surfaces that won't chip or scratch over time. If you do buy an inexpensive pot and it gets damaged, throw it away to avoid having your food react with the metal underneath or picking enamel pieces out of your pie crust.

Earthenware, clay and ceramic baking dishes are your taste buds' best friends in that they produce an effective form of infrared heat that allow flavors to develop over long roasting or baking times. These can be glazed or unglazed, but be sure to check the manufacturer's care instructions because many of these precious pots need pampering.

Copper pots attract chefs with their super heat conductivity and attract healthy home cooks with their antibacterial properties; just be sure yours is lined with stainless steel to prevent copper from leaching into acidic foods.

Pans

Sautéing and frying should be done in either enamel-coated cast iron pans, stainless steel or anodized aluminum.

Cast iron is long-lasting and conducts heat very well but shouldn't be used for liquids or acidic foods, because the iron can leach into your meal – not the form of iron your body craves but a rough-tasting and unusable form. Try Lodge-brand cast iron that's coated with nonreactive enamel and made in the USA. Some "pre-seasoned" Chinese pans are coated with toxic paint that can chip off into your food.

Heavy-gauge stainless steel pans are easy to use, but they need to be cleaned dutifully to avoid bacteria buildup in the tiny scrapes that steel wool inflicts. Use only soap, hot water and a soft sponge or soak it in baking soda to loosen hardened food residue.

Hard-anodized aluminum such as Calphalon, Cuisinart or KitchenAid is another good choice because the metals are sealed and can't creep into acidic foods like regular aluminum can.

> **What not to use:** Nonstick cookware in any form is too risky to be in your kitchen; the toxins, carcinogens and synthetics in these items have no place in healthy cooking. Aluminum is another metal that, like iron, the body can use in some forms, but not the kind in that frying pan on the shelf. Give all such items to a rhythmically talented child along with a set of wooden spoons for drumsticks and replace them with a few of the good-quality pieces above and you're off to a healthy start!

Baking sheets and forms

The best option for baking your cookies, muffins and breads is nonreactive anodized aluminum. Calphalon manufactures these pieces to keep the harmful metals under a seal. As always, clean with care using soft sponges and baking soda for harder spots. The next-best thing is Silpat's flexible, nonstick silicone forms and sheet liners. They're heat-resistant up to 428 degrees Fahrenheit and the only nonreactive synthetic material that is safe to use in your kitchen.

FYI

If you can't find or afford any of these items, simply line all your aluminum sheets and forms with natural parchment paper or paper muffin cups.

Kitchen appliances

To make meals happen fast, savvy chefs take advantage of time-saving appliances, most of which you probably already own! These tips will help you select convenient kitchen electronics and judge for yourself if yours are adequate.

> **Blender:** Anything over 500 watts should crush ice and blend smoothies well, but look for a brand you know and a good warranty so that you get the most out of your blender. There are also some nice middle price-range models from Cuisinart that double as food processors. Whichever model you choose, just be sure the pitcher is made of glass, not bacteria-loving plastic!

> **Food processor:** Unfortunately, you'll be hard-pressed to find a food processor with a non-plastic bowl on the U.S. market. Use yours properly and you won't have a problem with toxins: hand-wash in hot water and soap, take care not to scratch the surface and never put hot foods into the food-processor bowl.

> **Juicer:** When juicing fruits and vegetables, a centrifuge juicer is a time-saver and actually creates less waste, letting you get the most out of your food.

> Fragile nutrient bombs like sprouts, greens and wheatgrass need a low-speed twin-gear press juicer, which is the optimal means of pressing the delicate greens without losing any of the skittish enzymes in the process. One of the most frequently recommended brands is Green Star, which offers many models with optional components for more than juicing.

Bowls

Stainless steel mixing bowls are like practical, sturdy shoes: you can do anything in them and not worry about scratching them. You'll also want a few fabulous serving pieces – wooden bowls practically strut from kitchen to table when you're ready to serve a salad. Treat them gently, like you would a good pair of Louboutin heels, and keep them away from any sharp objects that could damage the surface. Always hand-wash your wooden containers and utensils to prevent warping, and allow them to dry in the open air.

Utensils

Before you buy a utensil, ask yourself what you'll use it for. If hot or acidic foods come to mind, go with natural, nonreactive materials such as wood and bamboo. Stainless steel is a safe choice for cold preparation such as chopping and whisking. Stay clear of plastics, rubber and aluminum in all your utensils.

Knives

Look for two things when selecting a set of knives: resistance to rust and lasting sharpness. The sharpest edge can be found on ceramic knives by Kyocera, but they don't have the flexibility of forged metal knives and can break if severely bent or dropped. Expert German cutlery makers Wusthof and Henckels both craft high-carbon stainless steel knives that are rust-free and nonreactive and hold their edge very well.

Cutting boards

Even the simplest kitchen needs two cutting boards, one for meat, poultry and fish and the other for vegetables and everything else.

Meat, Poultry and Fish: Stay a step ahead of salmonella and E. coli by keeping this cutting board separate from other ingredients while you cook and putting it straight into the dishwasher when you're done with it. The most practical boards for protein prep are flexible plastic mats like Norpro's set of four color-coded gripping mats. The colors help you to tell them apart; you can use red for meat, blue for fish, etc. And they're inexpensive. With proper cleaning, they should last a while, but do replace them from time to time as they become scratched.

Vegetables: Safely slice and dice foods that have been washed clean of bacteria on a wooden cutting board. Wooden boards have even been shown to have some antibacterial properties. As with all your wooden utensils, hand-wash in hot water with soap and a soft sponge or brush, then air-dry your board before storing.

FYI

If food odors linger after the first wash, rub coarse salt over the board with half a lemon, and then clean a second time.

When I go shopping for pots and pans, I love to see all the colorful boxes and promises of "easy" and "fun" – two things I always have in my kitchen! At first, anything that claimed to make cooking simpler or cleaning faster appealed to me, and as my collection grew, I thought, "My God, I'll never have to scrub a pan again!" But through a lot of research, I learned that the most attractive option isn't always good for my family's health.

appliances

Major kitchen appliances play a key role in your new healthy kitchen and whole food attitude.

Your stove should be where the magic happens; flavors develop, aromas abound and the result is delicious healthy fare. It doesn't take a miracle, but consider these helpful and healthy tips:

Gas is simply healthier than electric, the main reasons being control and natural energy. Gas heats faster and more evenly and is easier to regulate, because you instantly control the flame instead of waiting for an electric burner to heat or cool to another setting. This is also important in ensuring that your foods do not overcook, which leads to rapid loss of nutrients and enzymes.

The other consideration is that gas stoves emit no electromagnetic fields, which are known to disturb the natural rhythms of the body. This also applies to microwave ovens that potentially leak radioactive waves from the door during cooking. The further we remove ourselves from artificial sources of energy, the better we feel and the healthier we become.

Yara's Memories

As a girl, I used to despise my mother's gas stove because every day after dinner I was the one who had to roll up her sleeves and clean it. When I moved out on my own, I made sure that my apartment had an easy-to-clean electric stove and self-cleaning oven. After a while, I started making some of my favorite ethnic dishes and discovered that I had too little control over my oven. The amazing self-cleaning machine had its advantages, but if I needed to quickly change the temperature under a pot of lentil soup, it would boil over by the time the burner had cooled down. Now I have a nice old-fashioned gas oven and stovetop—just like my mother's.

A note for tea-lovers and time-savers

When was the last time you and your teapot spent some quality time together? Taking the time to brew a perfect cup of tea can lift your spirits even before you put your lips to your favorite mug!

Important to remember when brewing tea

- Start with cold, fresh filtered water; heated water from the hot-water supply or leftover from your last brew will have less oxygen (vital to releasing tea's flavor) and higher mineral content.

- Steer clear of electric kettles, which too often use nickel in their heating elements and plastics in their coverings, both of which leach allergens and carcinogens into the water.

- After boiling, let water cool for a couple of minutes before adding tea to keep the leaves from turning bitter.

- When possible, use loose-leaf tea, which tends to be of higher quality than tea bags. If you do choose tea bags, find ones in a cone or pyramid shape to allow full expansion and release of flavors.

- Each tea has its own steep time and for good reason – lengthy steeping results in lots of bitter tannins in your cup. So if you prefer a stronger brew, just add more leaves and stick to the appropriate steep times listed below.

Green tea	1-3 minutes
Black tea	3-6 minutes
Oolong (a blend of black and green teas)	3-6 minutes
White tea	5-8 minutes
Herbal tea	3-10 minutes

Heed my hints above and waiting for water to boil won't be boring anymore – just invest in a good-quality gas stove and a ceramic kettle from Mercola to avoid toxins. Sip, sigh and enjoy!

The refrigerator is too often a chaotic place and can harbor unhealthy bacteria. Here's how you can reform your fridge:

❖ Keep the correct temperature – the American Dietetic Association recommends 34 to 40 degrees Fahrenheit for refrigerators and zero degrees or less for freezers. Check up on older appliances by purchasing a thermometer and placing it inside for an hour or so before reading.

❖ The coldest areas of the refrigerator are the bottom drawers, where most people keep their fresh produce. Dedicate one of these drawers to storing your meat (potentially the biggest bacteria threat in the fridge), and leave the second for fresh fruits and vegetables.

❖ The door is the warmest area and should never be used for milk, eggs or other easily perishable foods. Better to keep your condiments, beverages and other lasting items there in tightly sealed glass containers.

❖ Devote your top shelf to cooked foods that need to be eaten within a few days, and always keep them separate from raw items. Prepackaged dairy is okay, but eggs in a carton are not. Save the second shelf for produce overflow (from your designated veggie drawer), eggs and anything else that hasn't been mentioned.

❖ Read Chapter 4 for new ideas about healthier storage. Proper packaging can not only make your food better for you but save you money by extending the life of foods and reducing waste.

❖ Keep it clean! Go through the refrigerator once a week (preferably just before your shopping trip, when it's looking empty) and reorganize.

- Remove everything and set it aside.

- Open a new box of baking soda and sprinkle it around each shelf, the door and inside and under the drawers.

- Using a soft, clean sponge and warm water, scrub all surfaces, focusing especially on the bottom, where spilled foods are likely to pool and bacteria are likely to grow.

- Wipe clean with a dry cloth.

- As you put items back into the fridge check for freshness and proper packaging. Throw away anything that looks questionable.

- If you haven't already heard about the Arm & Hammer Fridge Fresh Refrigerator Air Filter, you'll be happy to learn that by simply sticking it to the wall of your refrigerator, you can practically eliminate all food odors – even that Chinese takeout from last night (which you removed from the takeout box and put in a covered glass container, right?). The filter has its own indicator to tell you when to replace it, taking the guesswork right out. Find it at just about any grocery store.

Chapter Two

the pantry

review, revive and renew!

Healthy food starts in the pantry. From dry goods to the occasional canned ingredient, we can't cook, bake or prepare healthy meals until we've cleared out the junk and replaced it with wholesome alternatives. Yes, change is good! Don't worry – you won't be completely without snacks and sweets. But I know that with all the delicious whole foods in your house, it will be easy to let your appetite direct you to better choices.

Let's clean house! Take stock of your storeroom by first removing everything and setting it on a table. Spray your shelves with natural countertop spray and wipe clean. Now that your pantry is prepared, promise yourself that you aren't going to return the same junk to those shelves that you had there before. Get a pen and paper because you are very likely going to need a shopping list for the healthy pantry items below. If you already have some of these, great! Wipe them off as you proudly return them to their rightful place in your new and improved pantry. You know what to do with the rest – say good riddance to inferior items that have been sabotaging your family's health.

What Is Organic?

Just the facts:

- Organic food is grown without most pesticides and synthetic fertilizers
- Bio-engineering of plants, called genetically modified organisms (GMOs), is not allowed
- Food labeled "organic" must be separated from conventional items during growth, harvest, transport, storage and display to avoid contamination with chemical residues

No games:

All foods labeled "organic" have to meet criteria set by the USDA and receive this seal:

If you see the word "organic" on the label, this is what it means:

- The farm or company applied to the USDA for inspection by a certifying agent (all labels must include that agent's name).
- The farm or company has been USDA-certified (companies may choose not to use the seal on their packaging, but they must be certified in order to use the term "organic" to identify their products).

The real deal:

If the label reads…

"100% Organic" – everything inside is organic

"Organic" – 95 percent or more is organic; sulfites (preservatives) are not used

"Made with organic" – from 75 percent to 94 percent is organic but can't use the USDA seal

"Organic" in the ingredient list – less than 75 percent of the contents are organic, can't use the "Organic" label on the front of the package and may list organic ingredients individually on the back label

Yara's Memories

I grew up in a city, but we always bought produce from the farmers' market around the corner, and the grains we cooked came in burlap bags from a grower just outside of town. So to me, the American grocery store was a fascinating place. Canned soup and boxes of cake mix were a revelation, and I wanted to try them all. The first can of chicken broth I opened turned out to be extremely salty. The next one was better, but it took a long time and a lot of experimenting to find the best-quality convenience foods. I've done my homework and know what's safe and healthy to feed my family. Still, whenever I have the time, I try to make things myself, because nobody has figured out how to can the love in a bowl of homemade soup.

Your healthy pantry is sectioned into at least five shelves
containing the following:

shelf one:
oil & vinegar

Oils: You'll need two types of oil, one for high-heat cooking (frying, sautéing, baking) and
another for low-heat preparations (salad dressing, quick sauté). Many people ask, "Why
not use heart-healthy olive oil for everything?" because they've been told that oils low in
saturated fat automatically make for healthier meals. The short answer is that although
olive oil is indeed full of essential fatty acids like omega-3, any application of heat is going
to start breaking those nutrients down and create cell-damaging free radicals, making even
the healthiest of fats into a heart hazard!

Here are the oils you always want to have around the house:

1) Coconut Oil (high heat) – this is your "go-to" fat for anything involving high heat or long cooking times. It's full of medium-chain fatty acids, which are used quickly by the body for energy and aren't stored as fat. Tropical oils, like coconut, palm and palm kernel oils, won't oxidize or spoil as quickly as other fats, retaining their nutrients longer and contributing to your health rather than diminishing it.

Shopping Tip

If you like the mild flavor of coconut in your oil, go for Spectrum Organic "Virgin" Coconut Oil that has not been refined to remove odor and flavor. Spectrum Organic Refined Coconut Oil is recommended for those who prefer a tasteless fat; the refining does not create toxins like the processing of vegetable oil does. Coconut oil has a shelf life of about three years, so stock up! It is solid and white at colder temperatures, but turns liquid above 76 degrees. No need to refrigerate unless you plan to use it as a creamy spread in recipes.

2) Grapeseed oil (high heat) – here's another oil that can stand the heat of sautéing and frying. The smoke point is high, meaning that it won't turn your kitchen into a fire drill. I like to use it mixed with an equal amount of extra-virgin olive oil when I'm making anything hot that needs the mild flavor kick of olive oil. Its smooth taste makes it double as a nice salad oil for cold preparations. La Tourangelle makes a quality organic grapeseed oil that you can use for just about anything!

3) Olive Oil (low heat) – keep extra-virgin olive oil handy for dressings and anything you want to lightly sauté. It lends a Mediterranean flair to summer salads and matches up equally well to heartier fall flavors such as mushrooms and garlic.

Shopping Tip

It pays to be choosy about your olive oil because not all are created equal. Any vegetable oil that is not cold-pressed or expeller-pressed contains trans-fatty acids (famous cancer precursors). Get the best organic, cold-pressed olive oil you can afford, sold in a dark or opaque glass container – the less heat and light your oil has been exposed to, the better it is for you. If you see one labeled "single source," snatch it up – this is oil gained from one harvest of olives at one grove, ultimately providing the richest flavor.

Treat yourself to a nearly $50 bottle of Olio Taibi from Sicily and rediscover the joy of warm bread dipped in a saucer of smooth olive oil. It's available only online (read about the Taibi family that makes Olio Taibi & purchase from Amazon at http://theoliveoilblog.com/shop/), but it's worth the effort.

For more frequent use, get a larger bottle of Frantoia for half the price at natural grocery stores. It's packed with essential fatty acids, and the deep green color and fruity flavor make a superb salad oil. Frantoia cold-presses a blend of three Sicilian olive varieties and bottles the pure, unfiltered first pressing.

Use this key to olive oil classifications:

Extra-Virgin – The first pressing of olives extracted through purely mechanical means. This oil has the lowest acidity level of any olive oil (low acidity is the mark of good-quality oil).

Fine Virgin/Virgin – Extracted mechanically during the second pressing of olives. Low acidity but not as delicately flavored as extra-virgin oils.

Refined – Extracted through chemical and heat treatments from oil that was unfit for consumption in its raw form.

Olive Oil/Pure Olive Oil – A blend of refined and unrefined oils. Acidity is higher than in any of the unrefined types.

Light/Extra Light – Not a classification of olive oil as defined by the International Olive Oil Council, this is a creation of marketers for labeling a blend of any number of vegetable oils that contains some measure of olive oil. This is always highly processed and has very little true olive-oil flavor.

4) Other Oils (low heat) – You may want to experiment with other types of organic, unrefined oils for low-heat food prep. Nut and seed oils make a quick, tasty dressing when drizzled over mixed greens with an aged fruit vinegar. Some recommended combinations are:

- La Tourangelle Pumpkin Seed Oil and Lucini Fig Balsamic Vinegar
- A L'Olivier Walnut Oil and Sotaroni Sherry Vinegar
- Eden Selected Unrefined Sesame Oil and a mixture of San J Organic Tamari Soy Sauce and orange juice

Yara's Memories

The only oil I knew in my homeland was thick green olive oil, freshly pressed from my brother's olive grove in a stone mill. To this day, my favorite breakfast is fresh bread dipped into this emerald-colored oil and sprinkled with herbs. However, at the store I found myself confronted with a long shelf of all varieties of vegetable oil, each bottle more intriguing than the last. There were terms like "light" and "unsaturated" that I was unfamiliar with, so I set out to decode all the jargon. From my research, I learned how differently each one affects the body and how to use the right oil for the job, which is what I want to share with you here.

ALERT - Most Wanted Oils:

Criminal: Corn Oil
Real name: Malathion
Crime: Popular doesn't always mean pretty: the grain that corn oil is made from often contains the neurotoxin malathion, and you can bet your fritters that it's still present in the oil.

Criminal: Soybean Oil
Real name: Hydrogenization
Crime: The innocent soybeans we enjoy steamed as edamame or roasted as a crunchy snack get transformed from healthy oil into creepy trans-fats through the process called "hydrogenization." Swap it for coconut oil instead and get zero trans-fats.

Criminal: Canola Oil
Real name: Rapeseed
Crime: Famed for its tolerance of high heat, canola is living under an assumed name; rapeseed is a natural insect repellent and toxic to humans, too. Scientists have supposedly genetically engineered the toxins out, but given the pure, heat-tolerant options nature provides us, why risk it?

Criminal: Peanut Oil
Real name: Long-chain fatty acids
Crime: If a stranger offers you a shiny string of long-chain fatty acids, just say no! The body needs some of these fats but can make them very well on its own, thank you very much, and will hoard the excess as fat. Not to mention that peanut oil has been around the processing plant a few too many times for your scrupulous cells.

Criminal: Safflower Oil
Real name: Polyunsaturated fat
Crime: The polyunsaturated gang is a bunch of hooligans that fire off carcinogenic weapons called free radicals when exposed to oxygen, heat or light.

Criminal: Sunflower Oil
Real name: Dementia
Crime: Sunflower seeds have a reputation as a super source of vitamin E, but the oil-refining process replaces the benefits with health hazards. British researchers found the dirtiest secret: regular consumption could double your risk of developing dementia in as little as four years!

Criminal: Vegetable Oil
Real name: Free radicals
Crime: Anything labeled vegetable oil is simply a mob of the unsavory characters listed above mixed into one bottle. Just like the rest of these health robbers, "vegetable oil" is highly processed and often contains risky GMOs and free radicals (carcinogens).

Vinegar: Organic vinegar is fine to use once in a while to perk up your salad, but don't go making a daily habit of it. The sour stuff gets in the way of your body's natural absorption of nutrients. Since our goal is to make everything fresher and healthier, it makes sense to use lemon juice for most recipes and add herbs and seasonings for variety. Then keep a few full-flavored vinegars on hand for whipping up a salad in moments when you don't have the time to make dressing.

Shopping Tip

Beware of labeling tricks that might get you stuck with a bottle of artificially colored and flavored vinegar product. Anything that includes the words "flavor" or "flavored," such as "Apple Cider Flavor Vinegar," is just cheap white vinegar masquerading as one of your favorite good-quality vinegars. When you open a new bottle, be sure to close the cap tightly and keep it dark and cool for up to six months of storage. If you notice that your vinegar is becoming cloudy or develops a pungent smell, it's time to throw it out.

From all-purpose to adventurous, here's a rundown of the varieties:

Coming Clean: Plain white vinegar can be labeled a number of ways, including "white," "distilled" and "distilled white". Basically a chemistry experiment, this harsh acid isn't something you'd want to use in any recipes, but it is a powerful way to clean.

Apples of Eden: Apple cider vinegar is the most popular choice for cooking. The main difference among cider vinegars is that some have been filtered and some haven't. Do you like more apple cider flavor? Choose Eden Foods' Organic Unfiltered – those cloudy particles impart delicious tang and aroma. Want a basic acid to support other fine flavors? Go for the transparent, filtered variety from Spectrum Organics.

Pour on the Pouret: The better the wine, the tastier the wine vinegar will be (and probably pricier). If the manufacturer has aged the vinegar, it will have a mellower flavor than those bottled directly after production. Martin Pouret's imported French vinegars remind me of wine shopping: choose an aged white descended from muscadet grapes or a fragrant red of cabernet franc lineage.

Sparkling Vinegar: As with wine vinegar, the grade of the beverage boosts or busts the bouquet. True Champagne vinegar is imported from France by Martin Pouret, but you can find nice varieties made in the same fashion from domestic sparkling wine, like B.R. Cohn's.

Spanish Chic: Spanish Sherry wine is the base of another spirited vinegar. Sherry vinegars range from sweet raisin flavors to complex, oak tones depending on the age and variety of grape used to produce them. Columela 30-Year Reserva Sherry Vinegar is sophisticated and nutty, while Sotaroni Sherry Vinegar is aged to sweet perfection.

Craving Kyushu: Rice vinegars come from a range of places, each with its own subtle characteristics, but I recommend the Japanese Kyushu variety for its mellow flavor and mega nutrition. It carries an enzyme load five times greater than that of ordinary rice vinegar because it's made from brown rice instead of polished white rice. Mitoku-brand Kyushu vinegar goes through a year-long traditional aging process and is the highest quality among rice vinegars. If you do choose to venture into other types, stay away from seasoned rice vinegar, which has added salt and sugar. FYI: Rice vinegar is made from fermented rice and rice wine vinegar comes from the natural deposits in sake (rice wine). They taste similar and are equally healthy.

Balsamic Basics: So you're standing in front of a wall full of brown bottles, all claiming to be balsamic vinegar – what do you do? Well, don't fret; I've been there, too, and have a few pointers:

- Balsamic vinegar originated in Modena, Italy, and the best-quality, second-best-quality, third-best-quality and so on still come from that region. If at all possible, go for a bottle with "Made in Italy" on the label and the golden seal from the Consortium of Producers of the Traditional Balsamic Vinegar of Modena (try saying that ten times fast!).

- Even if it comes from Italy, read the ingredient list. There should be one or two items: wine vinegar/balsamic wine vinegar and grape must (these are natural deposits from the winemaking process that help the vinegar acidify). If you read "caramel color," move on.

- The longer that balsamic vinegar of any origin is aged, the richer it will taste and the less you need to use. Take your time reading the labels, because many producers are proud of the fact that they age their vinegar in wooden barrels rather than commercial stainless steel vats, and they'll write it on the back of the bottle.

- Warning: Impostor! Some "white balsamic vinegar" has nothing to do with balsamic vinegar at all. Instead it is inexpensively reproduced with regular white wine vinegar and added flavors to imitate the supple charm of Modesto's gorgeous grapes. Don't be fooled – if you want genuine white balsamic vinegar from true trebbiano grapes, go for a bottle of Baker & Olive.

- My recommendation for Italian balsamic vinegar is Fini brand – smooth, full-flavored and in the middle price range.

- My favorite domestic balsamic vinegar is O-brand California balsamic. It's aged for 10 years in oak and tastes sweet and round.

Create your own herbed vinegars in just two simple steps!

1. Wash and dry a large bunch of the herb of your choice. Common varieties are tarragon, dill, mint and basil, but feel free to experiment with any herbs whose aroma you like. Pack the leaves in a stoppered glass jar.

2. Pour good-quality mild vinegar to fill the jar and seal. Leave the infusion for at least a week; open it periodically to check its flavor. When the concoction is potent enough for you, remember to remove the herbs so that they don't continue to strengthen the taste. White wine vinegar, Champagne vinegar and apple cider vinegar are some mild options that will give you a delicate base for your creations.

shelf two:
salt & seasonings

Salt: There are only two kinds of salt that provide the full spectrum of minerals and trace elements the body needs: Celtic sea salt and Himalayan crystal salt. In contrast with table salt, which has been stripped of the elements, leaving only sodium chloride and added chemicals, these two types of natural salt go through minimal processing to arrive in your kitchen just as wholesome as when they were found. Celtic sea salt is hand-harvested on the Atlantic coast of France, while Himalayan crystal salt is mined by traditional methods from the mountains of Nepal.

Buy Celtic sea salt and Himalayan crystal salt at almost any health food store; there's no excuse anymore for subjecting your family to artificial sources of iodine. One serving of milk over sprouted-grain cereal (try Ezekiel brands – they're satisfying and crunchy) will cover your daily needs with a form of iodine that the body can actually digest.

Play with your food!

Other than these two all-purpose salts, which can be used for both cooking and "finishing" (sprinkling on top of foods after they're cooked), there are a wealth of good-quality fancy salts ranging in color, flavor and texture.

Here are a few examples of fun finishing salts that are safe to include in your repertoire:

DAS Hawaiian Black Lava and Red Alaea salts are both mixtures of sea salt with either black or red Hawaiian volcanic clay, called alaea. Try this mineral-rich salt in a spice rub.

Danish Viking Smoked Sea Salt comes from seawater that is evaporated over a fire of fragrant woods, which gives it a deep copper color and smoky flavor. Use sparingly on meats and fish and in potato dishes to lend a unique savory element.

India Tree Brazilian Sea Salt is captured naturally from shallow seawater ponds and gives a crunchy accent to steamed vegetables or edamame.

Vanilla salt is actually just good-quality sea salt mixed with the seeds of the vanilla bean. It pairs perfectly with both sweet and savory dishes, such as custards or baked sweet potatoes. You can make it yourself, as it has only two ingredients and takes no special treatment. I recommend starting with a mild-flavored sea salt, like Maldon Salt, as the base and Madagascar Bourbon vanilla beans. Store your concoction in a well-sealed glass spice jar in a cool, dry pantry on the spice shelf.

The scoop on salt substitutes: Potassium chloride is a mineral compound formed from potassium instead of sodium to produce a salty taste; however, it often has a bitter or metallic "off" taste. When confronted with small amounts, the body can flush it out, but larger concentrations become highly toxic to your system.

Before rushing to replace your table salt with an alternative chemical compound, consider that 70 percent to 80 percent of the sodium in most people's diets comes from processed or prepared foods, including restaurant food. So the most effective way to cut your sodium intake is to take matters into your own hands, and your own kitchen, by preparing fresh, healthy food at home as often as possible. When you're in control of the salt shaker, you'll develop a good sense of how much is too much.

Yara's Memories

Damascus has been the center of the spice trade for centuries. I love walking through the outdoor market and being welcomed by the scent of freshly ground cinnamon and the sight of bright red chile peppers hanging in bunches. Anything I need can be scooped from a tall pile of dried herbs or spices by a merchant with deep knowledge of seasonings in his ancestry. I miss getting simple ingredients from my family's farm in the mountains, like dried mint leaves that were gently crumbled between my grandmother's palms. Now that I don't have access to these special seasonings, I'm careful to investigate what I buy. Some packaging can be deceiving, and companies aren't required to tell you all you need to know about their products. I gathered all the important facts for my family's health, and you can use them as a guide to making your own healthy decisions.

Spices: Are you guilty of maintaining an everlasting spice rack? Go ahead; you can admit it to me because I've done it, too. When you cleared out your pantry at the beginning of this chapter, you probably found little jars of funky seasonings and herbs that have been opened and then forsaken behind the flour sack for months if not years. Well, now is the time to dump those useless and, by now, flavorless items for the seasonings you actually need.

Here are the basics you should always have on hand:

- Whole black peppercorns: As with any dried spice, make sure it's organic to avoid significant nutrient loss through irradiation
- Cayenne pepper
- Paprika powder
- Cumin seeds
- Coriander seeds
- Cinnamon sticks: Check for the word "Ceylon" on the label. If it's not there, you're getting a cheaper imitation of cinnamon called "Cassia," which is somewhat bitter
- A seasoning blend of your choice, such as curry powder or Chinese five spice – just be sure the ingredients are all names of spices you know, not chemicals you don't!

Spice up your health

Instead of selecting pre-ground spices, it's best to buy the whole version and grind it a la minute with a mini food processor or even a coffee grinder (they're so cheap you can have one just for your spices). You'll notice an immediate difference in aroma and increased flavor in your dishes.

Irradiation

This is the treatment of food with nuclear radiation with the intent to kill bacteria and insects. This process changes the food at a cellular level and eliminates organisms by mutating their DNA. The FDA does not have sufficient studies or regulators in place to make irradiated food safe for consumption, but it is trying to remove the international Radura symbol, which is currently required on all irradiated food products.

Shopping Tip

*When stocking up on seasonings, keep clear of generic brands when possible. Go straight for organic options like **Swanson Organic**. Otherwise, you could be dumping toxins onto your carefully prepared healthy foods. Most commonly you'll find additives in spice blends, seasoning mixes and almost anything with the words "flavor" or "flavored" on the label. Little bottles masquerading as "onion powder" or "garlic powder" are not healthy. Read the ingredient list on the back of every seasoning blend you purchase and if any of the following additives are among the contents, just say no!*

1) *MSG (monosodium glutamate): suspected neurotoxin, often from genetically modified sources*

2) *Aspartame: commonly used in sugar-free products; a known excitotoxin*

3) *Glutamate: recognized by the ALS Association as extremely toxic to nerve cells in high doses*

4) *Cysteic Acid: another exitotoxin found mainly in artificial flavorings*

Herbs pack the power to pick up your mood or even banish the flu bug, and they've done it for every civilization in history! Add a few herbal aromatics to your tea and to your meal because good nutrition is Mother Nature's disease-prevention plan.

Fresh vs. Dry

Honestly, fresh herbs are always better for the same general reason that fresh food is better: nutrients haven't had the chance to sneak away through the light and air around them. Dried herbs can be a time-saver, though, and are especially important in the cold winter months when they aren't in season. But don't buy into the myth that you have to get the ancient ones sitting on your grocer's shelf – you can dry them yourself!

Buy fresh herbs when in peak season, taking advantage of the high nutrient level and low cost. Get extra so that what you don't use right away you can dry or freeze for later use in recipes.

Delicate Herbs

Basil	Dill
Tarragon	Mint
Cilantro	Parsley
Chives	

Delicate herbs are best for freezing: After washing and drying them, separate the herbs into a few smaller portions. Wrap them in paper towels, place the bundles in plastic bags labeled with the herb name and date, then freeze for up to two months. If you need to keep them longer, dip clean fresh herbs into boiling water, then ice water to blanch. When dry, they can be chopped or left whole, frozen as above and used within six months.

Healthy Hint: please take the time to portion them into small bundles because defrosting and refreezing is like inviting bacteria over for dinner! This goes for anything in your freezer.

Hearty Herbs

Rosemary	Sage
Marjoram	Thyme
Oregano	

Hearty herbs are best for drying: Hearty herbs can dry hanging upside down in paper bags (poke a few holes in the bottom for aeration). Remove after two to four weeks and store in glass jars for up to one year.

Chef's Note: dried herbs and spices should be added near the beginning of cooking in order to release their oils. Hearty fresh herbs, like rosemary and thyme, can be added during the last 30 minutes of cooking time for best results. Most other fresh herbs, however, should only be added to hot food in the last five minutes of cooking to preserve their delicate flavor and aroma, which dissipate quickly under heat.

shelf three: baking supplies

Baker, Beware: You know the saying "You are what you eat," so imagine what you would look like on a doughnut diet. Now imagine a slender carrot or a shapely salad green. You get the idea. Baked goods are a rare treat, but when we treat ourselves to something sinful, we ought to do it right! I'll share with you the best baking ingredients for your pantry, because everything tastes better hot from your own oven.

Flour Power: Just about any diet book will leave you with a white-flour phobia, but what is all the hype about? Let's compare the percentage of original nutrients that remain after the milling process in bleached, all-purpose white flour with those in unbleached, whole wheat flour and you can draw your own conclusions:

White Flour	*Whole Wheat Flour*
(wheat flour after processing)	(whole grain, stone-ground)
50% Calcium	100% Calcium
30% Phosphorus	100% Phosphorus
20% Iron	100% Iron
2% Magnesium	100% Magnesium
15% Manganese	100% Manganese
50% Potassium	100% Potassium
35% Copper	100% Copper
20% Thiamin	100% Thiamin
40% Riboflavin	100% Riboflavin
15% Niacin	100% Niacin

Stone-ground

Just like our great-grandfathers used the mill, whole grains are still ground by stone into quality flour. The old-fashioned way keeps fiber and nutrients intact; no enriching necessary!

See the difference? Even "enriched" white flour contains synthetic forms of the vitamins that have been stripped in the refining process, which the body can't use.

Bleached

Yes, like your hair salon and laundromat, the food industry also uses chlorine bleach. Those golden grains of wheat are stripped of their fibrous outer shells, leaving the smooth kernel to be pulverized by machine and chemically brightened to snow-white "perfection." Most vitamins and minerals have already been left behind by this point.

Enriched

After the bleaching process, all those missing minerals have to be forced back in through yet another chemistry experiment called enrichment – stuffing synthetic vitamins into what used to be nutrient-rich food. Your body isn't dumb; it does know the difference and won't absorb anything that came out of a laboratory.

Baking with Whole Grains:

Use organic stone-ground whole wheat flour whenever possible; the grains remain more nutritious than in conventional refining. For a fluffier pastry or cake dough, you can substitute organic stone-ground white flour that is unbleached and mix it with an equal amount of stone-ground whole grain flour from Bob's Red Mill organic and gluten-free product line (garbanzo-bean flour is a delicious wheat alternative). Store whole grain flours in the freezer to keep the natural oils from becoming rancid.

Sweet Tooth: Moderation is the key to sweeteners; don't overdo it and you can enjoy a sweet little reward every now and then with no negative effect on your health. Read through the list of healthy options before your next shopping trip to see which sugar alternative is right for your pantry. Next, take a look at the facts below to encourage yourself in the smart decision to kick sugar out of your life!

Honey made the top of the list because of its near-miraculous health benefits: it supports the immune system, controls blood sugar, suppresses cough, fungus and bacteria, and even heals wounds. Buy Really Raw organic wildflower honey to get the most benefit and avoid falling prey to sugary scams (some honeybees are fed sucrose to boost production instead of letting them produce naturally from flower pollen). If you know you have a sugar problem (such as diabetes), ask your doctor first.
The Sweet Switch: 1 tablespoon honey replaces 1½ tablespoons sugar

Date sugar is perfect for baking, because it can be substituted equally for white or brown sugar in recipes such as cakes and cookies. It's high in fiber but doesn't dissolve in liquid well, so only use Chatfield's date sugar to sub for granulated sugar in baking and cooking. And as you might suspect, it's just dried, ground dates, so the nutritional benefits are sky high when compared with its refined relative.
The Sweet Switch: 1 tablespoon date sugar replaces 1 tablespoon sugar

Maple Syrup ranks high when it comes to liquid sweeteners because of its calcium and potassium content. Buy only bottles labeled "pure maple syrup," like Shady Maple Farms brand; otherwise, you may get an unnecessarily refined product with toxic additives or even a plain old bottle of corn syrup dressed up in an apron!
The Sweet Switch: 2 tablespoons maple syrup replaces 1 tablespoon sugar

Sucanat may not have been on the tip of your tongue when you last roamed the baking aisle, but natural grocers stock organic Wholesome Sweeteners-brand sucanat next to sugar (the name comes from the words **su**-gar **ca**-ne **nat**-ural). The brown crystals result from extracting the juice from sugar cane and allowing the water to evaporate. Sucanat is an excellent replacement for brown sugar in baking recipes and will dissolve equally well in warm liquids such as coffee and tea. It has a rich molasses flavor and retains all the minerals from fresh sugar cane, which refined sugars do not.
The Sweet Switch: 1 tablespoon sucanat replaces 1 tablespoon sugar

Here are the sugars and surrogates that didn't make the list, and why:

- **Agave nectar** is plant-derived syrup often hydrolyzed (chemically processed) or mixed with corn syrup, but it's hard to tell the pure from the polluted. A risky buy.

- **Stevia** is a calorie-free wonder plant in its natural form. If you're lucky enough to find the dried leaves, grind them yourself into a supersweet, fiber-rich powder. Stevia is much more potent than cane sugar, so use 1 teaspoon for each cup of sugar in recipes. The reason it didn't make my list is that all prepackaged Stevia on the U.S. market has been chemically altered from its natural form. So, unless you're intrepid enough to grow it yourself, chances are that the sweeteners listed above will make your life easier and sweeter, too.

- **Raw sugar** is the dried juice of sugar cane or sugar beet, before it gets the nature beaten out of it at the refinery to make the **white sugar** that surrounds us in processed food. Although raw sugar still has some nutrients, it would be a last resort for the health-conscious cook who just can't find any of the natural sweeteners listed above to put in his or her birthday cake.

- **Brown sugar** is the fake 'n' bake of the sugar world: it's originally white refined sugar that has spray-tanned itself with artificial coloring to look like natural sugar cane, which takes its brown color from molasses. What a phony!

- **Artificial Sweeteners = Chemical Charlatans**
  - ❖ *Sucralose* or Splenda is sugar modified to include the chemical chlorine.
  - ❖ *Aspartame* by any name (such as NutraSweet or Equal) is an excitotoxin – a poison damaging to the brain.
  - ❖ *Saccharine* is marketed under the name Sweet 'N Low and shows up in everything from diet soda to aspirin. Until recently, the FDA required that products containing this chemical additive carry a "may be hazardous to your health" label, and the American Medical Association still recommends limited intake of saccharine by young children and pregnant women – advice we would be wise to follow as well.

The bottom line: refined and artificial sweeteners will save you only 20 calories if you're willing to eat 20 chemical toxins.

Baking Soda and Baking Powder: All baking soda and baking powder contain some chemically enhanced ingredients – that's why they create eruptions at science fairs and uprisings in ovens – and there is no good natural alternative for getting a rise out of your sweet treats. But baked goods should be a relatively small part of your diet anyway, so minimal amounts will not affect your health.

You've already got baking soda under your sink for natural cleaning, but don't forget to grab a second box of Arm & Hammer for your cooking needs as well!

When choosing a baking powder, however, you'll need to take a look at the ingredients. Avoid anything with sodium aluminum sulfate, a common additive in commercial baking powders and boxed cake mixes (not that you'd stoop to using one of those). If you have a well-stocked pantry, you'll never have to reach for a boxed mix of anything again! Many health food stores carry Frontier baking powder, an aluminum-free, USDA-certified organic option.

If you suspect your baking powder is past its prime, test a half-teaspoon by placing it in a cup and pouring a third of a cup of hot water over the top. If the powder has power, it will bubble up vigorously; if not, throw it out and get a new aluminum-free organic powder.

Unwrapping Chocolate: Feel good about using organic, dark chocolate or cacao powder in your baking because it has an abundance of antioxidants: about eight times the amount found in strawberries! You can guiltlessly enjoy rich hot chocolate made from unsweetened cacao powder, but be mindful that it is naturally caffeinated. When buying solid baking chocolate, know that they're all made with sugar and dairy products. Use it occasionally in your baking-just remember to use sucanat as an alternative to refined sugar. Always take the darkest, highest-percentage-cacao chocolate you can find, because products like milk chocolate are only about 10 percent cacao, and white chocolate is made completely out of the fat in cacao beans (called cacao butter), so it doesn't contain all the nutrients I've been raving about.

*Buying only the best, certified-organic chocolate and cacao powder will give you maximum nutrient levels and premium flavor. Some organic brands to try are **Dagoba** and **Green & Black's** for fine cacao powder. **Valrhona** and **Domori** make superior solid baking chocolate out of rain-forest-grown beans, conched with care (gently rolled around to release full intensity of flavor). They are available in low-sugar/high-nutrient grades of 70 percent and above.*

Good Girl Cocoa

       6 oz. organic almond milk or soy milk, unsweetened
       1 spoonful raw organic honey
       splash of organic vanilla extract
       2 heaping spoonfuls unsweetened, organic cacao powder

Heat milk over medium heat just until it becomes steamy (no need to boil it, because that would ruin our enzymes).

Drizzle honey into the bottom of your mug, followed by the cacao.

Stir to make a thick paste.

Pour the warm milk into your mug, stirring as you do to dissolve the chocolate-honey mixture.

Add a splash of vanilla and take a sip!

Savor the rich chocolate and congratulate yourself for doing your health a favor!

__Vanilla__: This is one finicky plant! The orchid flower that produces our precious vanilla pods can be cultivated only in one of three tropical places: Madagascar, Mexico or Tahiti. Each region turns out beans with a specific look and aroma, but all of them take up to two years to ferment into the black beauty we recognize as vanilla.

The best beans for culinary uses are from Madagascar. High-quality Madagascar vanilla beans can be ordered online from Nielsen Massey. They are often called "Bourbon vanilla" after the French name for their island of origin and should appear shiny, black and moist. Mexican pods are thicker and strong-tasting but are often the victims of shady chemical additives; unfortunately, there is no guarantee that what you see is what you get. Tahitian vanilla is prized for fragrance over flavor, so it's best to leave those beans to the parfumiers of Paris.

Vanilla extract can be a quick fix for your desserts, but don't resort to imitation vanilla, which is full of chemicals and alcohol. Also steer clear of "vanilla flavoring," a mixture of pure and imitation vanilla. Look for organic "pure vanilla extract," such as Nielsen Massey's Madagascar Bourbon pure vanilla extract, made with the best ingredients and less alcohol. Do be careful not to add the luxurious liquid to hot mixtures or some of the essence will evaporate.

Almond extract in its genuine form is made only from almonds and when labeled "pure almond extract," like Flavorganics' pure almond extract. Imitation extracts are made from chemical compounds – not tasty.

Lemon extract is just oil from the fruit's rind preserved in alcohol; why not simply zest the peel off a fresh lemon? Only organic lemons are safe to use in your cooking, because conventional citrus has been sprayed with pesticides for all its growing life and no amount of rinsing will keep the chemicals out of your food. Wash your organic fruit well and grate the yellow peel all around just until the bitter white interior shows through. Use the sharpest, finest zester you can find; even the smallest cheese graters produce chunks, not delicate lemony zest. Substitute 1 teaspoon zest for ½ teaspoon lemon extract.

Other than baking goods, you'll want to have a few more items on Shelf Three:

In the thick of it: *The Truth about Gelatin, Starch and Aga-what?*

Without thickening agents in our food, we'd never achieve anything gooey, gummy, clotted or curdled (intentionally or by accident). Beginning with the good, here's a list of popular thickeners, with the bad and the ugly toward the bottom.

Corn, Potato, Rice and Tapioca Starches: All are safe, minimally processed thickening agents best-used in long-simmering recipes such as soups and stews. Wheat flour has a similar effect, but the whole wheat can leave unsightly brown particles behind, so stick to the four types listed above. Remember, I don't use white all-purpose flour for anything but papier-mache! Let's Do Organic brand makes natural tapioca starch and cornstarch, and organic potato starch is available from Frontier.

Agar-Agar: Don't judge a jelly by its name; nutritious as well as gelatinous, agar-agar is naturally taken from red algae. It's widely used in commercial dairy products, organic and otherwise, so chances are you've already eaten it! Pick up a packet of Eden Foods-brand powder or use it in thin strips, similar to gelatin, for firming up custards, puddings and jellies.

Xanthan Gum: Although the sources are natural, xanthan gum is extracted by chemical means. Studies show that it isn't toxic to the body, but some people are irritated by the allergens in its three source foods: corn, soy and wheat. You'll find it in organic products, so look at the label and try to find a brand that uses guar gum instead.

Guar Gum: Guar gum is as simple as it gets: seeds of the guar plant are dried, hulled and ground into powder. That's it! No allergens, toxins or unnatural processing.

Gelatin: You don't want to know. Trust me. But if you've been reading thus far, you also know that we're on a true health-finding mission, so we won't "sugarcoat" anything in our pursuit of the best health of our lives! Gelatin is a byproduct of the meat and leather industries, mainly derived from the leftovers of pigs and cattle. That's right – skin, bones, tendons and all make their way into almost every gelatinous product on the market. I told you so …

Pectin: Store-bought pectin is laced with toxic preservatives and requires sacrilegious sums of sugar to gel, so consider these alternatives:

- If you're using ripe seasonal fruit, it should already be sweet on its own and not need loads of cane sugar, which is why I recommend making preserves. Unlike jelly and jam, who seem to have a sugar addiction, a preserve is simply spreadable fruit, and once you've tasted it you won't go back.

  Wash and prepare your fruit, put it in a heavy pot with water just to cover and add honey or a splash of 100 percent juice (orange and cranberry are my favorites). Bring to a simmer and let the fruit stew slowly until most of the water has evaporated.

  Now it's time for **The Plate Test**:

  Put a spoonful of preserves on a plate, stick it in the fridge for a minute and then take a look at the consistency.

  Is it runny? Keep stewing.

  Can you spread it on toast without making a mess? Sounds about right, but you're in control, so keep stewing and using the plate test until you're satisfied.

- If you can't live without Grandma's jam, consider making an adjustment for the sake of your health: agar-agar (see above) needs no sugar to activate the gelling process and it's all natural. Read the packaging for instructions, but the rule of thumb is ½ teaspoon agar-agar powder for each pound of fruit. Pectin-rich fruits like apples, stone fruits and citrus will need less, so always start small, using the plate test mentioned above, and add extra powder as needed.

shelf four: canned goods

This shelf is like the ER of the kitchen. Together with the freezer, cans provide cooks with shortcuts that are sometimes necessary, but not without a price: prepared foods always lose some nutritional value in the process of manufacturing. In fact, canned foods only became popular during World War I, as a way for families to be prepared for the worst. Now the industry has changed its marketing to persuade the busy mom, the young bachelor and even children to eat canned food as a daily staple.

That said, here are a couple of items to keep on hand for "one of those days":

San Marzano canned tomatoes
Canned Pacific albacore tuna in water (American or Dave's)
Eden Organic No-Salt-Added Beans

Notice how short the list is! If you plan ahead of mealtime, you shouldn't need any of these things on a regular basis. After you've tasted tomato soup from vine-ripened summer "ugly tomatoes," you'll never look at the canned stuff the same way. But out-of-season tomatoes are grown by force and don't develop the same nutrition or flavor, which is where canned tomatoes can really shine: they're picked and canned when ripest and full of vitamins and quickly cooked to avoid the need for preservatives. If you're bored with winter vegetables and need a taste of summer, a can of organic San Marzano tomatoes will come in handy.

Tuna can be tricky, so keep a couple of facts in mind when you shop: all the big brands turn out a product with fewer omega-3's, more mercury and less freshness than smaller producers. A recent independent study by the University of Nevada tested the top three brands of canned tuna and found that more than half of the hundreds of samples contained mercury levels higher than the EPA's safety standard. Go to a natural food store and browse the aisles for a can of American Tuna or Dave's brand and know that you're getting more quality for your money; not to mention that these family-owned businesses test frequently for mercury levels and incorporate fishing practices that are safer and friendlier for both us and marine animals.

Any canned bean, vegetable, soup or other product is generally loaded with salt and chemical preservatives, so keep your emergency supply organic and no-salt-added. Better yet, try soaking some of the beans and other legumes in the next section to get 46 percent more fiber and 57 percent more folate into your new healthy meals.

Vegetables belong in the freezer wing of your culinary ER. Growers harvest the crops fresh and often clean and freeze them the same day so that what you defrost for dinner has almost as many vitamins as when it left the soil. The same can't be said for canned. Frozen organic veggies are the way to go.

Even organic broths and stocks can contain hidden MSG (carcinogenic food additive) in the form of hydrolyzed yeast or yeast extract, so use my recipe for homemade vegetable stock and freeze any extra.

Yara's Memories

Friday was the highlight of my week for the 23 years I lived in my parents' home. We kids got a break from our school-study-sleep routine and my mom made a big family-style meal from scratch. If she was making hummus, she had to soak the dry chickpeas overnight and boil them herself. If she made pasta, she chopped and stewed the tomatoes herself because there was no tomato puree at the market and certainly no heat-and-serve pasta sauce. Whatever she made tasted better for the love she put into it.

When you don't have time make your meals from scratch, it's okay to have some canned ingredients around for support. We all get busy, so just make sure you know what to look for on the label before you zip through the checkout line. I'm guilty of grabbing something off the shelf without reading further than the name of the food inside—this is extra tempting for me because English is my second language and the last thing I want to bother doing is read a bunch of fine print when I'm in a rush. But trust me, it's worth it to be selective about your groceries and get the best-quality foods for your health and your palate.

shelf five:
dried beans & grains

Grains Are Great

That goes for everything from side dishes to breakfast cereal. But beware of the words "instant" and "quick" on packaging – this means that the healthiest parts, the outer layers called "germ" and "bran," are gone and the kernel has already had the nourishment boiled out of it in order to cook faster. There are plenty of vitamins (B and E), fiber and essential minerals you don't want to miss in all three layers of the grain. Instead, soak grains for twice the recommended time and most will cook in just 20 minutes!

Soak up the benefits

All unpeeled grains, seeds and legumes (beans, lentils, peas) are immature plants. When we soak the dried kernel, it sheds an invisible guard called an enzyme inhibitor, allowing its nutritious personality to come out. That's why many of these foods are listed with soaking times; it takes a little encouragement to get the love out of a legume!

Depending on your ethnic background, your body may be wired to absorb nutrients from certain grains better than others. Generally speaking, a person of Asian descent would do well to introduce more brown rice, mung beans and adzuki beans into his meals; a Middle Eastern person's body will benefit from bulgur wheat, brown lentils and chickpeas; someone of African origin might mix more millet, teff and black-eyed peas into her diet; a European descendant will want to work buckwheat, oats and spelt into weekly meal plans; anyone natively from the Americas could consume quinoa, amaranth and lima beans often. No matter where you hail from, have the courage to try as many of these whole grains and legumes as you can find! Diversifying your diet will always give the body a chance to take in different combinations of vitamins, minerals and trace elements – and you may find a new favorite food in the process. Get many of the whole grains listed here from Arrowhead Mills organic brand at your local natural food store or from the Arrowhead Mills Web site.

- **Oats**: Try organic steel-cut oats and you'll never miss instant oatmeal, ever. Take the time to make a breakfast that will carry you into the afternoon satisfied and nourished. Just don't confuse steel-cut oats (cut-up whole grain) with rolled oats (pre-cooked twice, rolled out and toasted – the poor little grains have been through a lot!).

- **Buckwheat (kasha)**: A.k.a. whole-grain or buckwheat groats, this tastes great when you want a hot breakfast cereal that's ready as quickly as your coffee.

- **Bulgur**: This parboiled whole wheat grain makes a nutritious last-minute side dish for anyone bored with rice. The large-grain type pairs perfectly with lentils as pilaf, and the fine-grain type is an essential component of tabouleh salad. See the recipe section for more ideas.

- **Wild Rice**: Don't let the name fool you: wild rice is a seed! Higher in fiber and flavor than white rice, put it in the oven with a variety of vegetables and a little homemade broth to make a memorable casserole.

- **Barley**: Get hulled barley (the whole grain) and soak it for six to eight hours ahead to shorten cooking time and release more nutrients than the pearled variety (the polished inner kernel). You may already have tried it in soups and stews, in which case you know that barley is worth the wait.

- **Quinoa**: (pronounced keen-wah) This is a light, quick-cooking alternative to refined grains like cornmeal or couscous, which are missing their original nutrition. It is the ideal side dish because the seeds soak up sauces readily yet have a pleasant personality of their own.

- **Spelt**: The grain can be used anywhere wheat is called for in recipes, including as flour in bread and pasta dough. Mix it with other varieties in this list and create your own pilaf – just soak spelt overnight before adding to grains with shorter cooking times.

- **Kamut**: Whole kamut grain can be soaked overnight and cooked ahead and tossed with roasted vegetables and vinaigrette to make a flavorful salad that's high in protein and minerals.

- **Millet**: Bring out the most in your millet by toasting it briefly in a hot skillet before steaming or boiling. The seeds are rich in B vitamins and readily take on the flavors around them, making them an appetizing alternative to traditional bread or rice stuffing.

- **Amaranth**: The Incas prized it for its exceptional nutrition, as should you – try its nutty flavor mixed with rice or quinoa for an original complement to stir-fry. You can even prepare it like popcorn for your next movie night!

- **Teff**: A little-known wheat relative, teff is a great source of iron and calcium. The small size makes it great for grinding into flour to use for baking bread and thickening soup.

Make more, get more

Eating healthy doesn't mean being a slave to your kitchen! Make a few extra portions of whole grains while you're at it and keep them in the refrigerator for up to three days. Scoop a portion into a small saucepan, sprinkle with water and cover to gently steam over medium heat. They'll be just as nutritious and taste even more delicious because of the time you saved by making a double or triple batch the night before.

Store whole grains for six months in a dry glass jar in the pantry or for a year in the freezer.

Rice

Quick, how many types of rice can you name? Long-grain, short-grain, maybe basmati? Well, there's a lot more out there to be savored and much more nutrition to be had on our Rice Route:

Japan	**Short-grain rice** is sticky, as any sushi chef knows, and the basis for successful rice pudding.
India	**Long-grain rice**, such as **basmati**, makes a tender biryani and keeps any pilaf from sticking.
Thailand	**Jasmine rice** is also long-grained but lends a unique fragrant aroma to Thai fried rice.
Spain	**Medium-grain rice** is just starchy enough to stick together and when combined with saffron, tomatoes and various meats or seafood results in light, moist paella.

West Africa	**Brown rice** is often parboiled (partial steaming process that moves vitamins from the husk further into the grain) and cooked similarly to long-grain rice as a sauce-sopping companion to spicy groundnut stew (groundnut = peanut).
Malaysia	**Red rice**, especially rich in trace minerals, is cooked with coconut milk and served alongside a fish curry called nasi dagang during the holidays.
China	**Black rice** pudding (called juk) can be savory or sweet and was once reserved exclusively for the Emperor, due to its anti-aging properties – it has less sugar and more antioxidants, fiber and vitamin E than its weight in blueberries!

Many of the above varieties are available from Lundberg Family Farms, along with bags of blends that cook well together. Lotus Foods imports the more exotic types, many of them organic! Once you've opened a new bag, store the remaining rice in a well-sealed glass container for up to a year.

Legumes

That is to say, beans, peas and lentils! All the above will appreciate a bath in lukewarm water before cooking. The soak will allow them to release gas-creating enzyme inhibitors, making for smooth digestion and maximum absorption of nutrients. Throw out the soaking liquid and give them a good rinse in fresh water before cooking to get rid of any toxins that leached out overnight. Thorough cooking is another important way to destroy lingering enzymes that would prevent our bodies from digesting proteins.

Add salt or acid ingredients to legumes only in the last 10 minutes of cooking to avoid a tough, chewy result. After your beans are fully cooked (you'll know when you can easily smash one between your fingers) drain them and add to your recipe.

As a general rule, light-colored beans are higher in calcium and darker beans are rich in iron, but all legumes are low-fat sources of fiber, protein, folate, B vitamins, magnesium, potassium and phytochemicals (vegetable immune boosters). Pair them with a grain, like rice or whole grain bread to give your body a complete protein – all the amino acids necessary for bodily function.

Shopping Tip

Bob's Red Mill supplies natural food stores with an array of colorful beans, and Arrowhead Mills has an organic line of good-quality lentils and peas. Look at the bag when you pick it up – are there many broken or shriveled-looking pieces? Don't settle for a bag of bean dust. Old, poor-quality legumes will not cook well, so pick your peas prudently.

Use some of these seasonings to make any legume more digestible:

- Bay leaves
- Cilantro
- Coriander
- Cumin
- Fennel
- Garlic
- Ginger
- Peppers of any kind (fresh or dried paprika, cayenne, etc.)

Little legumes (mung and adzuki beans, green and yellow split peas, all lentils except for red) need only a 30-minute soak in lukewarm water before cooking. Add 4 cups of liquid for each cup of legumes and simmer partially covered for about 30 minutes. For red lentils, skip the soak and go straight to the next step.

Big beans and peas need to bathe overnight in fresh water to be ready for the stove in the morning. Add 4 cups of liquid for each cup of beans, and cook according to the instructions on the package, because every type varies slightly. Just like with whole grains, you can always make extra and store them for a few days in the refrigerator to make the most of your kitchen time.

Chapter Three

shopping

produce

local + organic + seasonal = your best health ever!

Did you ever pick a pickled pepper and wish you hadn't? Choosing your produce wisely is not just for Peter Piper! Buying the best organic produce in season saves you doctor's visits and money.

Sad but true: prepackaged lettuce is packed with gases and fungicidal waxes in bactericidal wrappers, all just to keep it "fresh" in transit – "fresh" meaning two weeks old in most cases. Even organic salad mixes are packed in nitrogen to look pristine up to ten days later. Taking five extra minutes to wash and chop your own head of lettuce from a local source, like the farmer's market or natural foods store, will save your immune system the nasty task of processing unnecessary chemicals. Local produce has not been marked up in price to cover transportation costs or sprayed or waxed with synthetics, is picked in season at the peak of ripeness and contains much more nutrients than its foreign cousins.

Organic produce is everywhere and for good reason. Here's a sample of the growing health evidence for organic over conventional produce:

- Organic fruits and vegetables tested in a four-year European Union study contained 40 percent higher antioxidant levels than conventional produce.

- Produce grown organically retains twice the minerals, according to the Journal of Applied Nutrition.

- Conventional produce grows under layers of herbicides, fungicides and pesticides. The EPA found that 60 percent of weed killers, 90 percent of 'shroom killers and 30 percent of bug killers are carcinogenic to humans.

Choosing seasonal produce means you're eating real food, the natural way humans have eaten for ages. Breaking nature's cycle doesn't do your body any favors – the earth provides all the nutrients your body needs at exactly the right time to keep you active and healthy. Try basil pesto in June or pumpkin soup in October and judge for yourself if it tastes better! That doesn't mean you can't have your fava beans in February, but it does pay off nutritionally and flavorfully if you pick the main ingredients in a meal based on what's in season.

As I mentioned in the pantry section, canned vegetables are generally loaded with salt and preservatives, so your best choice for an out-of-season ingredient is to forage the freezer for a bag. Organic frozen vegetables are picked at the height of flavor and nutrition and immediately flash-frozen to preserve as much of their freshness as possible. By the time you've defrosted them, they actually have better flavor and more nutritional value than an out-of-season item you picked up in the produce section. Remember that a greenhouse vegetable needs chemicals to grow because it resists the natural process of growth and harvest. I believe that science should be in harmony with nature, not fighting against it.

Yara's Memories One year my cousin wanted to celebrate my visit with a big, traditional lunch at his farm in the countryside. He and his wife worked hard to prepare a lovely meal that would feed our two families—after all, lunch is our main meal in Syria, and the best way to honor your guest is to arrange as many dishes in front of him as you can. My cousin, like most suburban and rural residents, has a large vegetable and herb garden, fruit and olive trees, chickens and occasionally a few sheep. He cooked one of the lambs he'd raised in his own pasture (a tradition for special occasions), and his wife cooked it skillfully with other ingredients from their land. It's funny how those who live simply and naturally think of farming as an obligation, while those in the fast lane just want to slow down and enjoy a vine-ripened tomato from their own garden.

meat

Pumping Plant Protein

Just because you can doesn't mean you should. Keep this in mind, dear reader, as you consider the small sampling of alarming information I've gathered about the meat we eat. The only two major diets that put animal protein on a pedestal are the typical bodybuilder's meaty meal plan and the controversial Atkins diet. Excepting these two extremes, the rest of the planet relies mainly on leafy greens and whole grains to fuel their bodies. Countless cultures make vegetarian or vegan dietary choices based on centuries of folk wisdom passed down to them. So if we consider the numerous plant-based diets versus the few animal-based diets, it is obviously healthier to go veggie!

When your body is nourished by plenty of fresh vegetables and whole grains, it isn't missing the meat. The protein your body absorbs from a steak comes directly from the green grass and grain that cow ate. And if you think that calcium is a natural part of milk, it is – because the greens that dairy cows consume are very high in calcium. Read on to learn more about meat and dairy and some plant-based alternatives to determine the best choice for you and your family. I understand that some people aren't willing to let go of all their favorite animal foods, but I want you to know the truth: your body is happier and healthier without them.

Back to the Future

Even in ancient civilizations where local food was the only food and people had to grow their own produce aisles, meat was an infrequent part of our ancestors' diets. If your forefathers were kings, sultans or wealthy landowners, chances are they had the meatiest meals of anyone in their societies – a few times a month, at most.

Once our local communities began developing into the globalized, middle-class-oriented nations we now dwell in, our diet also began to adjust to the "good life." In just the past 100 years, Americans have come to eat almost 20 percent more red meat and 450 percent more poultry. Not only would patriarch Pythagoras find this to be out of proportion, but the father of mathematics himself was a vegetarian.

So eating meat was a rare treat, but why go veggie? We now have more reasons than ever to cut down or cut out consumption of animals. Technology and industry have motivated major changes to the natural chain of how meat gets to your mouth. As nauseating as my research of meat processing proved to be, I want you to know the plain truth and use it to make your own healthy lifestyle choices.

Cannibals and Chemicals: You Are What You Eat

Conventional "range-fed" cattle start their short lives at home on the range, so to speak. At a few months old they are crowded onto boxcars for transport to equally crowded feedlots. The steers stand in their own manure, which can legally make its way back into their feed, and the chaos of cultivating the literal cash cow gets worse. Cattle feed on pesticide-ridden grains and the rendered remains of other animals (they used to eat their own until the mad cow epidemic forced an end to that practice). After their stomachs, which are designed for digestion of grass only, become bloated bacteria bombs, they are further filled with growth hormones and antibiotics (to combat the unsanitary conditions and improper feed). At sixteen months of age, herds of heifers are slaughtered in a stressful setting and meat is treated with radioactive isotopes to kill the strains of bacteria that have become resistant to antibiotics.

If the numerous health risks of this process don't turn you off to conventional meat, here's one other thought to ponder: if stress plagues human health with disease and premature aging, is it any wonder that the meat from a constantly stressed animal is of inferior quality?

The Organic Difference

If you can't live without the occasional steak, support the growing organic meat industry. The lucky son of a steer that is raised on an organic farm receives no growth hormones or antibiotics: they just aren't necessary when the animals feed on chemical-free pasture like their bovine ancestors did. At a well-stocked meat counter you'll have two options: 100 percent grass-fed or grain-finished organic meat. The difference is that the latter are taken off pasture toward the end of their lives and given organic grain feed to fatten them up before slaughter. The former is the only cow raised in completely natural conditions; however, both are far superior options to a conventional cut of beef.

Choice Cuts

Fresh beef is deep red with white fat around the outside (yellow fat is the result of unnatural feed). Ground beef will sometimes be slightly brown in the middle, or whole cuts might be almost purple inside, but this is just the natural color of red meat before it's exposed to oxygen. The leanest, most flavorful cuts available for simple grilling are top sirloin and sirloin tri-tip; for roasting or braising, choose the top round. Fresh-ground beef is the safest and most flavorful, so bypass the frozen burgers and ask your butcher to grind a good-quality piece of bottom round roast the day you'll cook it.

The Veal Deal

Conscious consumers have long shunned veal because of cruel practices on conventional calf farms. Unfortunately, calves are still weaned too early and forced to feed on milk substitutes in messy pens without access to the outdoors. It is this lack of natural light and movement that keeps the meat white and tender. But organic ranchers say it doesn't have to be that way: organically raised calves stay with their mothers (often dairy cows) on the pasture until they are humanely slaughtered for consumption. The result is veal that is pink, tender and easier on the conscience.

Choice Cuts

Select organic veal that's pinkish in color – white meat is the sign of an anemic calf.

Black Sheep, Black Sheep, Have You Any Worms?

Shepherds have a bigger problem than the occasional wolf: flocks are constantly exposed to worms and parasites living in pastures. Conventional breeders just attack the issue with chemical worming agents and send their enormous flocks to limited pasture. Organic breeders have had to come up with natural ways to win over worms, and they seem to be working. Small flocks of the best breeds are allowed to graze on clean, green pastures only after the morning dew has dried and worms have retreated back underground. It's simple but it works, and I'm grateful to the organic shepherds for providing us with natural, delicious lamb.

Choice Cuts

Good lamb is red with white fat around the outside. Young lambs are most tender, so look for small-boned racks and legs that weigh less than five pounds. Although the leg is leaner, a well-trimmed rack of lamb is a good choice and very tender. Sheep give birth in the spring, so choose U.S. lamb from March to June and New Zealand lamb from September to December (that's springtime in the Southern Hemisphere).

A Cleaner Pig Sty

Conventional pork has a similar story to beef. Overcrowding, improper feed, early weaning and lack of fresh air and sunlight create a stressful life, leading to a stressful death and poor-quality pork. Organic hogs have access to pasture almost year-round, eat organic feed in clean pens and are allowed to suckle the full term with their mothers. The humane conditions and absence of antibiotics and other chemicals create safe organic meat.

Choice Cuts

Good-quality pork is pink, never grayish. The natural layer of fat on roasts and chops is thin and even. Loin roast is the best choice for a very lean pork roast.

Nutrition Notes

Occasional consumption of organic grass-fed meat supplies the body with protein, essential fatty acids, B-complex vitamins, iron, zinc and phosphorus. Or you could get all this and more out of grains and legumes …. keep reading! If you do choose to indulge in the occasional steak, please be careful in your preparation: the National Cancer Institute warns against charring meat, because the process of over-grilling animal protein turns burned amino acids into carcinogenic chemicals (abbreviated HA and PAH).

Preservatives: Lengthen Shelf Life, Shorten Your Life

Children and women in particular must also pay attention to preservatives commonly used in processed meat products. Chemical nitrates have been linked to ten times greater risk of leukemia in children, and a weekly hot dog for pregnant women resulted in twice the chance of giving birth to a child with brain tumors. Nitrates can be found in most hot dogs and other cured meats, but not organic products. Choose all processed meat products from trusted organic brands such as Applegate Organics and Organic Prairie, which distribute their sausages, jerky and lunch meat widely among natural food stores.

Your Best Choice

If all the cow pies made by the meat industry are getting you in a stink, consider your options for a savory high-protein meal without the meat. Whole grains and legumes like brown rice, quinoa, lentils and beans supply fiber, minerals, B-complex vitamins and protein in a form that's more useful to your body than any animal protein. You can get all the amino acids (building blocks of protein) your body needs by adding two or more types of whole grains or legumes into your daily diet. And incomplete proteins can wait a full 12 hours in the body for another component to come along and finish the puzzle, so there's no need to stress over combining this with that.

Soybeans are a nutritious bundle of protein, calcium and iron — yes, tofu is full of the good things you'd expect to find in a lean cut of beef, without the negatives! Mori-Nu makes it in three levels of firmness: soft, firm and extra-firm. It's versatile in recipes, too, which you'll find throughout this book. Processed soy products, however, such as fake meats and protein powders often come with chemical residue and additives. If tofu is old news to you, the extra enzymes in fermented soy such as Lightlife tempeh and Westbrae Natural miso paste are worth introducing to your healthy kitchen.

Finally, seeds and nuts are good sources of fiber, protein, minerals and essential fatty acids. Sprinkle some flaxseed, chia seeds, pumpkin seeds or walnuts onto your dinner salad for a crunchy contribution of omega-3.

poultry

attention, mother hen

Just because it's white doesn't mean it's innocent. People in our obese society mistakenly consume huge portions of chicken and other birds thinking they're a healthy replacement for red meat to solve their fat and cholesterol conundrums. Not so! Poultry may be lower in calories than other meats, but it's just as susceptible to the same health hazards facing other animals. Drugs, antibiotics and pesticide residues can all make their way onto the dinner plate and into our bodies.

Don't Call Them Chicken

Conventional chicken coops can house up to 40,000 birds pecking around in their own waste under near-constant artificial lighting, but that's not the most shocking thing you'll see on a modern chicken farm. "Mutants" is the first word that came to mind when I discovered that conventional birds can no longer bear the weight of their own oversize breasts; stimulant drugs cause such rapid growth that a chicken's legs cannot support its bloated body. The immobility, coupled with unnatural lighting designed to encourage extra feeding, makes antibiotic treatment a necessity for keeping the animals alive just long enough to bring to slaughter (about forty days).

Organic chickens, on the other hand, are granted days in the outdoors, dark sleeping quarters at night and an organic diet free of antibiotics.

Talking Turkey

Less than one-tenth of 1 percent of turkeys bred in the United States are organic. The rest are inbred from one busty breed that has lost the ability to fly, run or reproduce independently in favor of huge white breast meat. That gives turkeys and swimsuit models something in common: you just know those breasts aren't natural! The crowded, stressful environment they live in does no good to the quality of the end product either – the only justification is in the pockets of the producers.

Organic turkeys are more diverse and have access to the outdoors, pasture and organic grain feed. In my savory opinion, the natural lifestyle suits them.

A Duck Out of Water

Conventional waterfowl, such as ducks and geese, are literally raised completely indoors. Away from their natural habitat, the birds become stressed and dirty. Their organic cousins, however, get plenty of time at the community water hole and all the organic grain they can squawk for.

At the Meat Counter

Are you still stubbornly planning that chicken dinner? Okay, enjoy it this time and then try some sunflower sprouts for your plant protein. When you buy poultry, choose the best birds possible. Whole hens should look plump, with skin intact, free of punctures and tears. Whether whole or in pieces, buy organic "air-chilled" meat to avoid higher contamination risk and up to 8 percent greater water content from the slaughtering process. All poultry is leanest in the breast, but the leg is more tender.

Natural vs. Organic

Plainly put, a "natural" bird has received no additions to its natural state after slaughter – i.e., artificial colors and flavors. Unfortunately, what happened while the chicken was alive is not mentioned (probably because most consumers don't want to know). Consider yourself warned.

The organic poultry industry goes a step further to include organic feed, which is free of pesticides and GMOs and guarantees humane conditions from hatch to slaughter.

Free-range or free-roaming doesn't guarantee anything except an open door on the side of a potentially packed hen house. Producers are not required to shoo their animals out that door, and the "birds of a feather flock together" instinct keeps many flocks from ever using the exit. This is just another sad example of manipulative marketing, and most Americans have already fallen hard for it. In my opinion, the creators of these terms deserve a prize for the most ingenious scam in the industry.

In any case, thank God you're not a chicken! Also know that there are so many complete sources of nutrients in the plant world that you don't always have to peck around the poultry case for protein. Soybeans are extremely protein-rich, dark leafy greens provide most minerals and B vitamins, and all protein from plant sources is more readily absorbed in the digestive system. The occasional baked or roasted organic chicken breast provides protein, B-complex vitamins, niacin, phosphorus, selenium and zinc; dark meat also contains iron.

seafood

Remember the adage "There are other fish in the sea"? Well, that may have been true in your mama's time, but today our societal seafood habit is no longer sustainable. Overfishing has led to short supply, which in turn leads to fish farming: a treatment of the symptom, not a cure for the problem.

Born to Be Wild

Oysters may wear pearls, but they were never meant to be "cultured." Any mollusk labeled "cultured" or "cultivated" has been raised by humans in a water tank on land or a cage on the coast. These clams, mussels and scallops act as a natural filter for anything in their environment, whether it's algae in the wild or their own waste in captivity. The result: a shellfish is only as sanitary as its habitat.

And if cultured shellfish have even a percentage of the problems faced by farm-raised fish, that is one crazy fraternity. When fish are crowded into a tight space, it makes them more vulnerable to disease, and any slight infection can spread like pinkeye on Greek Row. The treatment: vaccines, antibiotics and disinfectants to keep scaly brothers healthy for party after teeming party. Their feed can only be dubbed "junk food," as the contents could never be found in a wild fish's diet: soy, corn, wheat pellets, growth hormones, chemical dyes and synthetics. Maybe worse are the carnivorous salmon and tuna, which receive a steady supplement of fish oil and loads of our already-depleted supply of wild fish.

So our supposed solution to overfished waters is actually eating up more of the wild seafood population. Every year many of the domesticated fish escape from their offshore cages to fraternize with the wild sororities of their species – exploits that expose the untamed sisters to the same dangerous diseases present in captivity. Current lobbies to allow genetic modification of farmed fish threaten to unleash Frankenfish on the pure DNA of anyone in the wild with whom he mates. Not to mention that lack of responsible labeling legislation means that between conventional farm-raised and genetic mutant, you'll never know the difference.

Age of Aquarius

Like everything on Earth, seafood has its seasons. During their summer spawning period, wild fish should be given their space. Ask your fishmonger what is in and out of season, especially from April to August.

Likewise, shellfish and crustaceans consume large amounts of algae that are potentially toxic to humans during what is called a "red tide." In the United States, this natural bloom of algae happens most often between May and October, so be sure your shellfish comes from a reputable supplier that has the means to test for toxins.

The old rule of thumb for oysters is to eat them during months that contain the letter "R" (anytime but May through August).

When your favorite fish is out of season, you do have another option: frozen. If the package reads "F.O.S." it means that the fish was caught in season and frozen at sea, right on the boat. If you live inland, this is always your best bet for the freshest fish, and you don't have to guess how many days it took to arrive at the seafood counter.

Toxic Tides

The good news is that safe seafood is becoming more readily available to all of us. Wild, deepwater ocean fish caught in the Pacific and Atlantic is a nutritious delicacy. Foreign-caught fish that has been frozen at sea from areas like Argentina, Chile, Mexico and New Zealand is among the purest and appears at most well-stocked groceries.

But oh, the bad news! Unfortunately, our coastal waters, inland canals, lakes and streams have become dangerously polluted with pesticide runoff and industrial residues. It's just not worth the risk of accumulating neurotoxins like mercury in the brain, which takes years to flush out of our sensitive systems. The older and larger a fish becomes, especially if it is higher up on the food chain, the more toxins build up in its fatty tissues.

Species regularly found to flunk the toxin test include:
Barracuda, bonito, buffalo fish, bluefish, farm-raised and river catfish, carp, corvina, croaker, eel, halibut (domestic), herring, lake trout, lobster (domestic), mackerel, mullet, pike, porgy, rockfish, sablefish, striped bass, freshwater bass, shad, shark, sturgeon, swordfish, trout (domestic), tuna (yellowfin, bluefin, albacore), chub, white perch.

The FDA and the EPA recommend that expecting mothers limit intake of seafood in general to twice a week and species from the above list only once a week. I recommend less frequent meals of the fish above – after all, if it isn't good for the baby, it probably isn't good for Mom and Dad either.

Omega Issues

If so many fish are contaminated, what about fish-oil supplements? In studies of popular fish-oil brands, mercury levels were relatively low, but experts estimate that between 25 percent and 50 percent of all fish oil sold in the United States is rancid before you even open the bottle. A potential solution to the problem of instability is a tiny relative of the shrimp called "krill." An antioxidant called "astaxanthin" naturally protects krill oil from becoming rancid, so no extra processing is necessary to keep it fresh. Krill is so low on the food chain that it doesn't have the chance to ingest mercury and other toxins in the frigid Antarctic waters it calls home. Researchers found that it not only boosts the body's omega-3 production more effectively than fish oil but it also lowers levels of lipids (fats) in the liver and cholesterol in the blood. Bonus!

The body needs several types of omega fatty acids, most of which come from animal sources. Take one capsule of Neptune Krill Oil per day and round out your omega needs with one tablespoon of Navitas Naturals chia seeds – they're much more digestible than flaxseed, so all you need is a spoonful in your morning oatmeal to get the remaining omega-3's that animal sources don't provide.

The Fishmonger

Get to know your grocer; the man behind the mussels is your best source for determining what's fresh and what's fishy. Ask what's in season, what's just been delivered and where it all came from before you decide what to buy. Some general guidelines are:

- Whole fish is firm, has shiny skin, bright-colored gills, clear eyes (as it loses freshness, the eyes become cloudy) and no slime. Freshly cut fillets are moist but not slimy, have no dried or browned edges and shouldn't smell fishy.

- Live crustaceans move their legs – pick up your lobster before you buy it and make sure it dances!

- Raw oysters must be properly refrigerated at all times – if it's not on ice, don't eat it. The shells should be tightly closed and not give off any strong smells.

- All shellfish is alive if the shells are still closed; open shells can harbor bacteria and should be thrown out. Anything already shucked (taken out of the shell) is not fit to be eaten raw – cook it thoroughly and enjoy it without the risk of food poisoning.

Wild fish don't carry the "Organic" label because they are nearly impossible to patrol in their natural habitat. I would much rather eat the wild unknown than consume the known drugs and synthetics fed to farm-raised fish.

Cockles in the Kitchen

Because fish store toxins in their fatty tissues and internal organs, you can minimize your exposure exponentially just by taking a few precautions when cleaning and cooking the catch of the day.

Prep:

Whenever possible, remove fish skin, innards, fat and tomalley (the paste inside lobster and shrimp heads) to keep many toxins out of the cooking process altogether. Always marinate raw seafood, poultry and meat in the refrigerator, not at room temperature. Then throw away the used marinade – never use it in your cooking!

Cook:

Studies show that you can reduce your contact with toxins by up to 65 percent just by discarding the oil from pan-fried fish. I suggest you practice this with all meats. A safe internal temperature to aim for in seafood is 145 degrees F.

> You'll know it's done when:
>> Fish flakes apart when you press lightly on the thickest part
>>
>> Shrimp turns pink and lobster turns red
>>
>> Mollusks open their shells (if they don't, throw them away)
>>
>> Scallops become opaque and firm

Fish Food

Most fish is high in protein, iodine, selenium, and vitamins A and D. However, some species are best eaten only on rare occasion, due to high cholesterol content. Also remember that all the freshwater fish and some of the saltwater fish in this list are vulnerable to more toxins than others, so they should already be on your radar.

Freshwater fish with high cholesterol:
> Carp, catfish, pike and rainbow trout

Saltwater fish with high cholesterol:
> Bluefish, Atlantic cod, mahi mahi, eel, grouper, haddock, herring, lingcod, mackerel, pollock, sablefish, salmon, sea trout, striped bass, tilefish and whitefish

Shellfish and crustaceans can be sources of protein and minerals such as zinc. But shrimp, crab and lobster are mostly just sources of cholesterol and calories.

One Warning: Multiple Causes

The most frequently reported food allergy among adults is to seafood. The reaction varies from a slight rash to full anaphylactic shock (deadly throat swelling that blocks airways). Some form of "allergic reaction" affects 7 million American adults, most commonly between the ages of 40 and 60. Although often reported as allergy, studies are showing that these reactions can come from another deadly source: poison. We know that toxins abound in many waters and can make their way into the digestive systems of fish and humans alike, but there are several poisons out there making seafood-eaters sick and it often gets blamed on allergy.

Histamine fish poisoning comes from many species of fish associated with sushi, such as tuna and mackerel, as well as sardines, mahi mahi and bluefish. When fresh, these raw foods are a delicacy, but if left out unrefrigerated, the growing bacteria raise the histamine content, causing reactions in diners that mimic allergies. Always enjoy your raw and cooked seafood from sources that you know have fail-safe refrigeration, practice proper food handling and have high product turnover.

Paralytic shellfish poisoning is the result of eating shellfish high in biotoxins from the algae bloom in a red tide. Cooking the affected animal will not kill the toxin, so it's better to avoid it altogether with the advice of an expert. Ask the fishmonger what's in season. No clambake is worth risking your health.

Tropomyosin is the protein responsible for most seafood allergies. It can even cause reactions in very sensitive people through the cooking process when proteins splatter out of the pan and into the air. But avoiding seafood may not totally keep you away from tropomyosin's effects. Common dust mites also carry the protein and can cause cross-reactivity in allergy-sufferers. If you have a known seafood allergy, take precautions in your home to keep clear of the offending bugs.

Yara's Memories

I used to love shopping for the sterile Styrofoam packages of meat. It all seemed so clean and neat, with every cut wrapped and labeled, ready to simply toss into my shopping cart. That got me thinking about how meat is purchased back home. We call the butcher on the day we want to cook and find out what kind of animals were delivered that morning. Then we go to the shop and the butcher carves off a piece of meat right before our eyes, exactly to our specifications. We had the same routine for buying fresh fish from the pier in our Mediterranean town. Whichever fish's eyes sparkle back at you determines what's for dinner. Sure, the fish market is not a pretty place, but the catch of the day is practically still jumping. Now there's often a long distance between the consumer and the source, so that food is unnaturally preserved to survive the journey from its pasture or stream to the deceptively packaged container in the supermarket.

dairy & eggs
scary moo-vie

Baby mammals can't live without the nourishment of their mother's milk. Yet only one species of mammal drinks milk greedily into adulthood and even transforms the secretion of other species into dairy delights: humans. Milk is meant to transform a newborn calf into a heavy heifer eight times its birth weight in just a year. Human children triple their weight in the first year but grow at a comparatively slow rate of just four pounds per year as toddlers. If this fact doesn't strike a chord with you, take a look at the truth about nutrition in dairy.

Nutrition in Milk

	Milk Fat %	Protein %	Carbohydrate %	Calcium mg	Phosphorus mg	Vitamin C mg
Cow	3.5	3.5	4.9	118	93	1.0
Goat	4.0	3.2	4.6	129	106	1.0
Sheep	7.0	6.0	5.3	193	n/a	2.5
Human	4.0	1.1	9.5	33	14	5.0

As you see in the table above, human milk is different from any other mammal's milk for a reason: we don't grow like farm animals! So what about the cliché that milk is the best source of calcium and vitamin D? One cup of milk has 300 milligrams of calcium, but the high animal-protein content makes it less usable to the body. One cup of cooked kale boasts 200 milligrams of calcium and a higher rate of absorption by the body. If you're not a fan of kale, just about any dark green vegetable will provide similar benefits. Also, a half-hour of moderate sun exposure is enough for most bodies to produce their own daily dose of vitamin D. Overall, our calcium obsession is unnecessary, and high doses of supplementation lead to kidney problems.

That said, dairy products have long been a traditional part of world cuisines and I don't expect many of you to completely cut them from your diets. But if you're going to go lacto, please choose the best!

$ Cash Cow $

Yes, American dairy farmers have been provided with a literal cash cow: they call it BGH for "bovine growth hormone." A conventional dairy cow produces up to 60 percent more milk than an animal on an organic, hormone-free diet. How is this possible? Bovine growth hormone (BGH) increases milk production through raised insulin growth factor (IGF-1) – the presence of high levels of this factor in a study of U.S. women raised the risk of breast cancer by seven times and also elevated risks of colon and prostate cancers. Pasteurization and processing do not destroy IGF-1 in milk, so any dairy product from conventional cows can contain risky levels.

If you're still tempted to go for cheaper conventional milk, think of this: dairy farms confine cows to sheds where they sit in their own manure until milking time. Pastured cows do their business outside and come in for milking with clean udders.

Grass-fed or "pastured" cows produce milk with a naturally lower fat content, higher nutritional value and more essential fatty acids such as omega-3. However, not all organic farms pasture their cows. Organic dairy means:

- Product comes from cows fed an organic diet with no animal byproducts
- Pastures where grass-fed cows graze are chemical-free
- No antibiotics or hormones are allowed
- Grain feed does not contain genetically modified material

Organic farmers often test milk for pathogens that could harm humans, while conventional dairy farmers just send it off to be pasteurized at ultra-high temperatures that kill bad bacteria and good nutrients/enzymes. Ultra-pasteurized milk, even of the organic variety, has a shelf life of six weeks – is that what you would call fresh?

Organic Valley brand uses regional suppliers to bring fresh local milk to each area they sell to. This eliminates the need for aggressive pasteurization. Regular pasteurization is enough for local products.

A Big, Fat Dilemma

Cow's milk is a source of calcium, linoleic acid, iodine, magnesium, phosphorus, protein, selenium, vitamins A, B, C, D, E and zinc. It is also high in milk fat. But before you go ordering a "skinny" latte or grabbing a gallon of skim milk, you should know that the body uses fat for more than just love handles.

Many of the nutrients in the list above are fat-soluble, meaning they are absorbed through the digestive tract with the help of dietary fats like milk fat. Taking the natural fat out of milk throws its entire nutritional profile out of sync. In fact, all whole foods contain cofactors – interdependent elements of nutrition that won't help our bodies unless in the company of all their natural allies. For this reason, many dietitians recommend that anyone who needs to supplement with vitamins do so with the help of tablets made exclusively from plant sources. New Chapter brand supplements are widely available in natural groceries. Even more potent are the LifeGive brand supplements easily ordered online from the Hippocrates Health Institute (bonus: the capsules are made of vegetable cellulose instead of wax).

Here's the skinny on fat in milk products:

Skim milk is fat-free but also has lower bioavailability of nutrients due to the lack of natural milk fat as a cofactor for absorption.

Low-fat milk has most of the natural fat removed. About 1 percent remains.

Reduced-fat milk is slightly lower in fat than natural milk, about 2 percent.

Whole milk is homogenized (process of skimming fat away from milk, decreasing the size of milk fat molecules and reintroducing them into the milk) to make a uniform fat content of 3.25 percent. True whole milk, as taken from the cow, varies between 3.6 percent and 5.2 percent fat.

Half-and-half is a mixture of equal parts milk and cream. It runs between 10.5 percent and 18 percent fat.

Whipping cream is largely milk fat, making it thicker and creamier. The fat content of light cream is about 30 percent while heavy cream contains 36 percent or more.

Buttermilk is whole, reduced-fat or low-fat milk thickened slightly with bacteria cultures to achieve a smooth consistency and tart flavor. It may be labeled "cultured buttermilk" and is often pasteurized.

Acidophilus milk is typically low-fat or skim milk with added cultures, similar to yogurt, to benefit the digestive tract.

The Solution

Choose the best-quality milk and dairy products to benefit from their nutrients and enrich your favorite foods. Always buy organic products labeled "pastured" or "grass-fed," and look for local brands or farmer-owned co-ops such as Organic Valley that bring you good-quality products over short distances for maximum freshness. Last but not least, heed your parents' advice to eat your vegetables and play outside – your body will thank you!

Your Best Choice

As you learned above, cow's milk is not the best source of vitamins and minerals for your body. Just one cup of tofu would give you 400 milligrams of calcium and 20 grams of protein - that's 130 percent of the calcium in a glass of milk and 250 percent of the protein! If that weren't enough proof, scientists have found that osteoporosis is most prevalent in countries where calcium is consumed from animal sources, probably because plant sources are full of proteins that help the body absorb other nutrients like calcium, whereas animal proteins block our uptake of calcium and other essential nutrients.

Let's compare the choices of nondairy milk for nutrition and uses, and then do your own taste test at home.

Soymilk	**Rice milk**	**Almond milk**
Smooth, milky texture	*Thin consistency*	*Creamy liquid*
Most protein and fat	*Most carbohydrates, least fat*	*Fewest calories*
Drink, cook, bake with it	*Just drink it – too runny for most recipes*	*Drink, cook, bake with it*
Unsweetened or flavored	*All are sweetened, some flavored*	*Sweetened or unsweetened*
Organic Valley, Eden Soy	*Rice Dream*	*Pacific Natural, Almond Breeze*

Yara's Memories

In my mama's kitchen, my job was to stand in front of the pot of fresh milk and watch that it didn't boil over. It seemed like the worst chore at the time, but now I miss those days of rich whole milk straight from the dairy farm. She'd strain the raw milk through a sieve into a big pot and boil it to prevent bacteria (that's when you'd see me with a big wooden spoon stirring aimlessly and daydreaming). Finally, she poured it into a cup and served it with crumbly sesame cookies for dunking. The fresh milk always had a layer of cream, too, so my mama would skim it off the top of the pot and set it aside for us kids to enjoy at breakfast. The rest went into glass bottles in the fridge for later. Now everybody gets pasteurized milk in paper cartons, which is all well and good, but I still miss my big wooden spoon and cup of creamy milk.

Eggs

The incredible, edible egg can do a lot, but it can't provide every nutrient the body needs, so switch your daily Denver omelet to a more diverse breakfast. I'll help you enjoy the transition with the delicious recipes in this book.

The Cholesterol Clash

One egg will run you two-thirds of your entire day's cholesterol limit or even exceed it if you're someone who already struggles with high blood cholesterol. All that, however, is hiding in the yolk while the egg whites are calling you cholesterol-free! A whole egg provides the body with biotin, folate, iodine, iron, pantothenic acid, phosphorus, protein, riboflavin, selenium, tryptophan, vitamins A, B12 and D. To get all the benefits of eggs in your meal, try substituting two egg whites for every other egg in your recipe, or just making your favorite omelet out of egg whites only.

Decoding the Carton

Organic Eggs: hens ate an organic diet, free of GMOs and animal byproducts, but were not necessarily raised outdoors.

Organic, Pastured Eggs: chickens ate grass and ran in open spaces – the yolks are bright orange, taste fresher and contain 10 percent less fat, 40 percent more vitamin A, 400 percent more omega-3, and 34 percent less cholesterol than conventional grain-fed chicken eggs because of their natural diet.

Omega-3 Eggs: regular chickens were fed flaxseed to imitate the nutritional value of pastured eggs.

Cage-Free/Uncaged/Free-Walking Eggs: this only means chickens weren't in a metal cage, but they could well have been crowded into a shed by the thousands.

Free-Range Eggs: this guarantees access to the outdoors but doesn't require that birds actually spend time outside the shed.

Natural Eggs: are regular eggs that were not treated with chemicals after gathering – that's not saying anything about what happened before gathering.

Farm-Fresh Eggs: means nothing! This is a manipulative marketing term used to imply freshness and the idyllic pastoral image. Your average chicken shed hardly looks pastoral and is probably more ideal for the farmers' pockets than the hens inside.

Sayonara, Salmonella

At the grocery store, always check eggs for cracks before purchasing. Not only do cracked eggs spoil, but salmonella bacteria can seep in (it's normally found on the outside of the shell from fecal matter but can also come from poorly raised hens who have sickly ovaries). Buy pastured eggs in good condition and save yourself the risk of infection. Always cook eggs through, and when making food that calls for raw eggs, such as creamy salad dressings or desserts, use pasteurized eggs to be certain that bacteria is not present. Fresh eggs should last about two weeks, but pay attention to the expiration date because part of that time has already expired in transport. That's why local farm eggs are the best choice, if you can find them. Organic, pastured eggs are your next-best bet. And don't fret over the question of "brown or white?" Shell color has to do with the breed of the hen that laid the egg and nothing else.

Your Best Choice

Just like meat and milk, when it comes to eggs you have more options than you realize! Protein from whole plant foods is more beneficial to your body than a boring breakfast of eggs and bacon. Shake things up in the morning with a fruit smoothie and some sprouted-grain toast with almond butter; rich and satisfying meals don't have to be heavy or lacking in nutrition.

Good news for bakers, too!

Many recipes calling for eggs can be easily improved with these substitutions:
   Applesauce, mashed bananas, pureed silk tofu or ground flaxseed and water replace **egg in baked goods**

   Rolled oats, bread crumbs, nuts, tomato paste or cornstarch have the **binding properties of egg**

   Soymilk replaces **egg wash to glaze pastry dough**

   Visit this website for more exact substitution rules: www.vegancoach.com/vegan-baking.html

Yara's Memories

One of the joys of visiting my mama's house is her generous breakfast buffet. The kitchen table is always filled with little plates of my favorite foods, and among them is a bright orange omelet. She gets her fresh eggs several times a week from my cousin's farm in the countryside. He lets the hens roam the pasture chasing worms all day and hand-feeds them grain, leftover vegetables and pretty much whatever remains from his family's meals. Actually, the chickens are as well fed as his children! The result of all that love is a yolk so vividly colored and a taste so extraordinary that I make it a point to eat them every time I visit.

Cheese

Our ancestors have been making raw, unpasteurized cheeses for centuries. While the first aged Stilton Blue could have been a fortunate accident by the fromagier's apprentice, it wasn't continued just because they liked the taste. The longer cheese ripens, the more healthy enzymes it develops. When looking for high-quality cheese, remember that all dairy is only as good as its source (read: buy organic for sure!). Cheese is a prime domain for concealed chemical residues that tend to gather in the fat molecules of milk (fresh cheese has up to 12 percent fat, while ripened cheeses range from 20 percent to 30 percent).

You can recognize good-quality organic cheese by the certifying seal on the label:

Domestic artisan cheeses carry the USDA organic seal.

European cheeses are labeled with the EU organic seal.

No Whey

Conventional cheeses are full of additives that preserve and give texture to otherwise-bland products. Especially avoid pre-shredded or sliced cheese, which is surrounded with chemical additives to expel moisture from the packaging. Seventy percent of U.S.-produced cheese is curdled with genetically modified chymosin instead of the natural enzyme rennet, which has been used for thousands of years to separate milk into cheese curds and liquid whey. But the worst of the worst are no doubt processed cheese products – you'll probably recognize most of them as items marketed to your children with bright orange artificial colors and deceptively creative wrapping. These have nothing to do with cheese except imitation dairy flavor from powders and oils.

Smart shopping pays off for your family's health. Organic cheeses contain no artificial ingredients and are produced without any GMOs, including chymosin – just organic milk and natural strains of good bacteria that are already present in our intestines. So experiment bravely with new sorts of cheese, both domestic and foreign. You'll find that your new favorite is just sitting there, ripe for discovery!

Butter

Like cheese, butterfat is a prime hideout for toxic substances. In fact, researchers found conventional butter to have 30 chemical contaminants – another good reason to go organic. Butter from grass-fed cows has considerably more nutrients and essential fatty acids, so look for packaging that proudly promotes its source as "grass-fed," such as Kerrygold Butter, or "pastured," such as Organic Valley's Pasture Butter produced locally by its co-op of farmers; it has the added benefit of being cultured.

While you wouldn't want to include butter in your everyday meals, for a rare treat cultured butter is a great choice because it is allowed to develop beneficial enzymes and more flavor. Generally, organic unsalted butter is made from the best-quality milk and doesn't require added salt to mask inferior flavor. One word to watch for, however, is "light"; these products are mixed with water or air, giving less buttery content for more cash.

Margarine is closer to plastic than butter on a molecular level – it's packed with artificial flavors and colors, hydrogenated and otherwise modified oils (sources of carcinogenic trans-fats and GMOs) and preservatives. That's enough to keep me miles from a margarine tub.

Yogurt and Friends

One of my favorite breakfast foods is yogurt. Try Stonyfield Farms plain organic yogurt with live active cultures over organic granola, or Oikos organic Greek-style yogurt (thicker and creamier) with a simple bowl of freshly cut seasonal fruit drizzled with raw honey.

All yogurts have to contain at least two active cultures, but some are then heat-treated (check the label), which kills the beneficial enzymes. Buy only organic yogurt with the National Yogurt Association's "Live & Active Cultures" seal to be sure you're getting maximum benefit from your yogurt.

Live & Active Cultures

*Meets National Yogurt Association Criteria for Live and Active Culture Yogurt

These enzymes and bacteria boost the immune system, balance the body's bouquet of intestinal flora and bestow comfortable bowel movements on those who normally can't digest dairy products.

Other organic dairy products to enjoy in moderation include:

Organic Valley

Cottage cheese

Ricotta

Sour cream

Alden's

Ice cream

Ciao Bella

Gelato

Take the time to browse your local natural food store. Have fun and resist the urge to compare organic or nondairy foods to their conventional counterparts. Just think of all the grand gastronomy you've been missing by sticking to the same old staples of the American diet! Some of my favorite things in the nondairy aisle are:

Whole Soy & Co. plain, unsweetened organic soy yogurt – same healthy probiotics as dairy; use as dressing, dip or sub for sour cream

Thai Kitchen organic unsweetened coconut milk – subs perfectly for cream in recipes, and a spoonful in hot beverages tastes sinful!

Organic Valley unsweetened soymilk – mix 1 C nondairy milk and 1 Tbsp lemon juice for a buttermilk sub (think biscuits or waffles)

Spectrum Organic coconut oil – unrefined is better than butter in sweet recipes; refined is better for savory dishes (sub 1:1 ratio)

Purely Decadent coconut-milk ice cream – an occasional treat in coconut almond chip, passionate mango and many other flavors

Yara's Memories

My grandmother makes the best yogurt. She starts with fresh whole milk from a neighboring dairy farm, boils it and, when the temperature is just right, does what no chef is ever allowed to do: she sticks her pinky finger into the warm milk and counts, "One, two, three, four, five ..." If she can hold her finger there for ten counts, the milk is cool enough to become yogurt. If not, she must wait for the right moment, when the healthful bacteria are primed to grow and thicken the milk. Then she adds the secret ingredient for making yogurt: a spoonful of yogurt! The next morning, if all has gone well for the bacteria produced by her secret ingredient, the pot will be full of creamy yogurt.

bread

the rise of whole grains

Hot, fresh bread has become a scarce commodity in America. Add to your wish list terms like "organic," "100% whole wheat" and "preservative-free" and you'll be baked by the time you find the perfect loaf. The first breads, flatbreads such as pita and tortilla, were made with only three ingredients: flour, salt and water. In France, French bread is allowed to contain only flour, water, yeast and salt. Now there are people who respect tradition! Where has our respect for fresh, simple ingredients gone, you say? The way of the mega-grocery: more, More, MORE!

Unfortunately, the demand for uniform varieties in every store, lower prices in lieu of good-quality ingredients and time-saving or shelf-life-lengthening additives has virtually killed our bakeries. The little guy just can't hold on in the face of chemicals that complete an hours-long process in only a few minutes.

Compare the labels on these two breads (from Margaret Wittenberg's "What to Look for on a Bread Ingredients Label." NEW GOOD FOOD.); both are commercially made, but have little else in common:

Sandwich Roll No. 1

Enriched wheat flour (unbleached flour, niacin, reduced iron, thiamine mononitrate, enzyme, riboflavin, folic acid), water, leavening (yeast, calcium sulfate), high fructose corn syrup, partially hydrogenated soybean, cottonseed and/or canola oils, egg, sugar, salt, vital wheat gluten, datem, dextrose, monoglycerides, calcium sulfate, ammonium sulfate, dough conditioners (ascorbic acid, sodium stearoyl lactylate, ethoxylated mono and diglycerides, enzymes, calcium dioxide, azodicarbonamide), emulsifiers (datem, mono and diglycerides), guar gum, cellulose gum, azodicarbonamide, modified food starch, citric acid, preservatives (potassium sorbate and sodium benzoate), xanthan gum, proplylene glycol alginate.

Sandwich Roll No. 2

Organic wheat flour, organic whole wheat flour, sea salt, yeast

Conventional loaves are loaded with an average of 25 ingredients (this one has 36), along with some additives in small amounts that are not even required to show up on the label. The four ingredients in this organic product are looking tastier yet!

Going Against the Grain

We know that organic bread is made with good-quality, chemical-free ingredients, but many of us don't realize that it isn't necessarily nutritious. The only way to get the whole nutrient profile that grains have to offer is to buy bread made out of whole grains.

Here's a list of labels we often associate with "healthy" baked goods and what they actually mean:

Enriched – after being cheated of its nutritious outer layers, the ground wheat was corrupted with cheap synthetic vitamins and minerals

Bleached/Unbleached – ground whole grains are not one uniform color but a beautiful mosaic of beige and umber-shaded speckles. In their naked form, however, they become mostly beige (unbleached) and are often chemically treated to appear "pure" white (bleached).

Multi-grain – these products were made from two or more types of grains (e.g., wheat and spelt) but not necessarily the whole grains.

100% _____ (fill in the blank with any combination of the following: plain, refined, untreated, stone ground, high protein, etc.) – All these claims mean little, and none of them denote a nutritionally superior product except when combined with the words whole grains.

The Whole Grains Council is industry-sponsored, and not every commercial bakery pays to be in the program, but if you find a loaf labeled with **seal A**, you're getting at least **8 grams** of whole grains per serving. **Seal B** is reserved for products made with **100 percent whole grains**, which contain at least **47 grams** per serving.

A) some whole grains, at least 8g

B) 100 percent whole grains, at least 47g

Below are the only ingredients you'll ever knead for homemade bread:

1. **Flour**: The healthiest bread is made from **whole wheat flour**. Whole wheat makes a denser loaf because the gluten (a strong protein that gives structure) content is low and doesn't allow many air bubbles to form under the crust. **All-purpose flour** has more gluten protein, so many bakers mix the two to lighten up their loaves (about a 1:1 ratio). Nutritionally, however, anything other than whole wheat flour is missing a lot because most of the vital outer layers of the grain have been removed.

2. **Yeast**: The friendly fungus ferments when introduced to flour and water, giving rise to bubbly baguettes and richly flavored rolls. Alternatively, some bakers savor sourdough: a whole loaf will rise from one tiny piece of last week's dough. After each batch, a section is severed and left to mingle with the wild yeast floating around in the air. The yeast starts to grow with the starchy support of the flour; after a few days, it's called a "sourdough starter" and is ready to rise again.

3. **Salt**: Yeast needs salt for the opposite reason that it needs starch: salt is the slacker that keeps the carbon dioxide that yeast produces from overwhelming gluten's structure. It also enhances the natural flavors of all the ingredients in the dough.

4. **Liquid**: Once water or milk is added to the mix, things really get moving. Gluten proteins in flour become elastic like a balloon, yeast activates and fills the balloon with air, and dissolving salt signals to stop so the balloon won't explode.

   If you're not a dairy fan, some great milk substitutes that can be used for baking are soy and almond milks.

   Rice milk won't work, because it has too little fat; conversely, coconut milk is too thick.

   1 cup soy or almond milk = 1 cup dairy milk

5. **Sugar**: Cane sugar, brown sugar, honey and molasses are natural flavor and color enhancers for a rich, brown loaf of bread. Commercial bakers take it too far, however, adding loads of sweetener to lengthen the shelf life of their dinner rolls and so on.

6. **Eggs**: Eggs are a valuable addition to some recipes, lending flavor, color, finer consistency and a tender crust. Challah and brioche are two famous sweet breads that rely on eggs for their delicate texture and flavor.

7. **Fats**: To keep bread moist, some recipes call for butter or oil. Baked products off the shelf generally contain hydrogenated vegetable oil or margarine (scary chemical concoctions) to stay looking "fresh" for weeks.

To those of you who already go whole grain, way to go! But why not take your good health even further and choose sprouted whole grains? The grain has been allowed to germinate (the first step in growing a new plant), which converts carbs to protein and liberates the nutrients to be more readily used by the human body. Bakeries then grind the nutritious and nutty-flavored grains into meal, and add yeast, water and salt. The final product is indescribably scrumptious bread — taste it for yourself and decide with all your heart, mind and taste buds to go all the way to your best health ever!

My favorite way to eat Food For Life sprouted grain bread is toasted with raw chunky almond butter. Also try Alverado Street Bakery sprouted whole wheat loaf with fresh hummus and crisp sliced veggies.

Yara's Memories

I spent my summer vacations on the sunny Mediterranean coast. We would drive up to the mountains every weekend to see my grandmother, and that's where I learned to make bread. Flatbread is an important part of our cuisine. I watched my grandmother knead a huge ball of dough and take it to her traditional tannour oven. She made flat rounds and stuck them to the sides of the hot oven, which had been prepared with blazing coals. When the dough began bubbling, it was time to remove it. Those warm pieces of bread dipped in dark, earthy olive oil, covered with chopped ripe tomatoes from the garden and sprinkled with salt made mealtime a joy at her house. And she had to do this strenuous task only once a week, because the bread would stay fresh for days with only a towel to cover it. The pure ingredients ensured that her loaves wouldn't spoil and needed no preservatives.

Chapter Four

storage

Smart Storage Secrets

By now you should be saying to yourself, "Nonreactive cookware: check! Organized healthy pantry: check! Seasonal produce and organic groceries: check!" Think you're ready to cook? Not quite. You've made the decision to stock your kitchen with healthy foods, but there are more methods of drastically cutting your chemical exposure. They start with the cleaning products under your sink…

Under the kitchen sink

What you'll need

- Veggie Wash – removes waxes, soil and other things you really don't want in your salad! Even organic produce can be waxed to protect it during shipping, so spritz the sprouts and rub those rutabagas thoroughly before rinsing well in cold water. Clean food = healthy food!

- Natural dishwasher detergent

- Natural dish soap – find one of the brands below or use castile soap instead of generic dish soaps. Don't be worried that bubbles aren't forming while you wash - the natural surfactants in castile soap (compounds that loosen dirt during washing) have the same effect as chemical versions but without the potential health threats.

- Glass cleaner (or make your own)

- Countertop spray (or make your own)

- Baking soda

- Vinegar

- Lemon essential oil

- Natural sponges with loofah or hemp for scrubbing

- Stiff brush for oven/stovetop

How to care for your supplies

You may have the right tools, but don't forget that they need a little TLC. Put your sponges and brushes in the dishwasher every other day to scald the bacteria and mold that creeps up around moist kitchen gear. The natural sponges should also take a 30-second trip through the microwave once a week to stay in top shape.

How to find it

The government doesn't require that conventional cleaning products' full ingredient lists be disclosed, and this is all the better for the manufacturers of these household toxins. The

SALT

Olive Oil

most commonly found culprit is bleach, which contains chlorine and lye-two of the original components used in chemical warfare! So what is it doing in your kitchen?

Luckily, most health food stores stock a range of natural cleaning products made without any of the poisons present in mainstream cleaners. Naturally manufactured products are often more costly, but isn't saving your family's health worth more than saving a few cents?

Some natural cleaning brands are:

Seventh Generation – makes dishwasher detergent, dish soap, glass cleaner and almost any other household cleaning product you can think of.

Mrs. Meyers – makes products similar to other natural brands' but focuses on lovely smells such as lemon verbena and geranium to keep you smiling while you clean.

Twist – makes the natural sponges listed above as well as cloths, brushes and other useful things.

Veggie Wash – the easiest way to clean fruits and veggies, and it's distributed far and wide, so you're bound to find it almost anywhere you look.

How to make it

If you're ready to roll up your sleeves and do it yourself, these cleaning tips are surprisingly easy and use simple items already present in many kitchen cupboards.

- Glass cleaner = 1 cup vinegar + 1/2 cup water + 15 drops lemon essential oil (fights grease and masks the strong scent of vinegar). Combine all ingredients in a spray bottle and shake before using.

- Disinfect the kitchen sink and make it sparkle with baking soda. Wet all surfaces, apply a liberal sprinkling of baking soda, scrub with a brush and rinse. Your faucet needs only a splash of vinegar on a damp cloth. Rinse and dry with a microfiber cloth to prevent water spots from forming.

- Kitchen countertops should be disinfected after every time you cook with baking soda and water. Combine 4 cups water with 3 tablespoons baking soda, dip a soft cloth or sponge into the solution and wipe over every surface. Let sit at least 20 minutes and then rinse with clean water and dry. This is safe for any surface, including marble countertops.

- Oven cleaner is as simple as vinegar and baking soda. Spray the vinegar over the inside of the oven and sprinkle baking soda throughout. The combination will get fizzy and loosen grease in about 30 minutes to an hour. Have clean water on hand and a stiff brush for scrubbing it off. If any grease lingers, just dip your sponge in vinegar and wipe the dirt away. Rinse with clean water and you're done! Oven racks fit in most dishwashers, so give them a spin once a week to degrease. And **never** heat your bread or other foods directly on the oven grill – that's what you bought cookware for! Ovens and stovetops may be clean, but they're still artificial surfaces, so play it safe and keep all edibles inside the cookware, please.

Clean, Mean Health Machine

How you clean your food affects its nutrition and appearance, both of which need to be at their best for your family to enjoy the full benefits of good-quality ingredients. Before unloading your grocery bags, read these tips:

Produce

- **Greens** and other dainty produce should be kept in their bags on the bottom shelf of the refrigerator to keep them cold and free of moisture. Only when you're ready to use them should they be washed, dried and chopped – nutrient levels plunge faster than you can say oxidation! Place individual lettuce leaves in cold water with a splash of apple cider vinegar and gently rub any sand off the outer leaves. Rinse twice in fresh water, air-dry or dry on recycled paper towels in a pinch. Any unused leaves can be wrapped in dry paper towels and stored in a zip-top bag labeled with contents and date. Remember to cut only what you need. Light + oxygen = death to vitamins!

- Keep hardier **fruits** and **vegetables** in one of the bottom drawers of the fridge (the coldest part) until you need them. Take out only what you'll use immediately, spray it with Veggie Wash and rub well to remove waxes and residues (conventional producers use petroleum-derived shellac and fungicides; organic certifiers allow beeswax and a few other non-chemical solutions). Rinse well with cold water and air-dry before using; otherwise, you just water down the recipe. Fresh **mushrooms** come cleaned from the producer but should be wiped with a moist towel to remove any lingering soil; never rinse them or submerge them in water, because their spongy caps will soak it up and become mushy.

Meat, Poultry & Fish

- All the above should be used within a day of purchase or frozen for later. It's up to you to practice safe handling of these products so that your family can eat safe and healthy meals. Keep them in their own dedicated drawer in the bottom of the refrigerator, and clean it after every use. Rinse raw **meat**, **poultry** and **fish** in cold running water just before cooking, and then dry well in paper towels. Be dutiful about using countertop spray or vinegar to disinfect every surface that comes into contact with the raw meat – including your hands! Use a separate cutting board for raw meats and vow never to let a stray vegetable appear on it.

It's a Wrap

Leftovers are a precious product of your hard work, so don't waste them with improper storage. Let food cool on the kitchen counter for up to one hour and then transfer from cookware to glassware; metal pots can leach toxins when used as long-term storage containers. Popular plastic containers are an even worse choice because the carcinogens

they contain are proven to migrate into acidic and fatty foods during storage, even more so when heated in a microwave. Pyrex makes glass storage bowls with airtight covers that keep anything fresh for a day or two. Place them on the top shelf of the fridge along with prepackaged dairy products and anything else that isn't raw meat or produce.

When you want to freeze foods, take a moment to portion them individually. Refreezing anything is risky business that you don't want to be involved in. Also be diligent in labeling containers with dates and descriptions, because many things start to look alike in the back of the freezer. Be patient when it comes time to defrost – several hours in the refrigerator is the only riskless method, but a cold-water bath is an acceptable shortcut as long as the food is heated through and eaten right away.

Plastic Perjury

Not many manufacturers would admit to it, but the plastics industry is not exactly producing better living through chemistry. Easier, yes; better, no!

Offender: Clingwrap covers everything from prepackaged produce to chicken thighs to sliced cheese. Fatty foods easily pick up traces of the carcinogens DEHP and DEHA used in the covering.

Alternative: Buy whole products and slice them at home; ask for meats and fish cut right in front of you to get the freshest product wrapped in butcher paper.

Offender: Waxed paper and parchment paper are often coated with dangerous formaldehyde.

Alternative: Choose natural parchment paper for baking and storing foods; if the label says "natural," it isn't permitted to contain formaldehyde.

Offender: Microwave packaging for products like popcorn, pizza, French fries, fish sticks and frozen waffles are dangerous when heated. The waves disintegrate some packaging, transferring dimethyl terephthalate to the foods inside (yet another suspected carcinogen).

Alternative: In a perfect world, you would make all your own snacks with good-quality ingredients. But if the kids are screaming and you need it now, at least take the food out of the original packaging and heat it safely on a ceramic plate or in a glass storage bowl.

Offender: Aluminum foil is especially dangerous when used with acidic foods such as tomatoes and citrus because it has been proven to leach metal over time.

Alternative: Cover foods while cooking with natural parchment paper or use a covered glass container to store them.

Offender: Plastic wrap leaches carcinogenic vinylidene chloride and other toxins, into foods, especially when hot.

Alternative: Covered glass bowls make storage toxin-free, as does natural parchment paper.

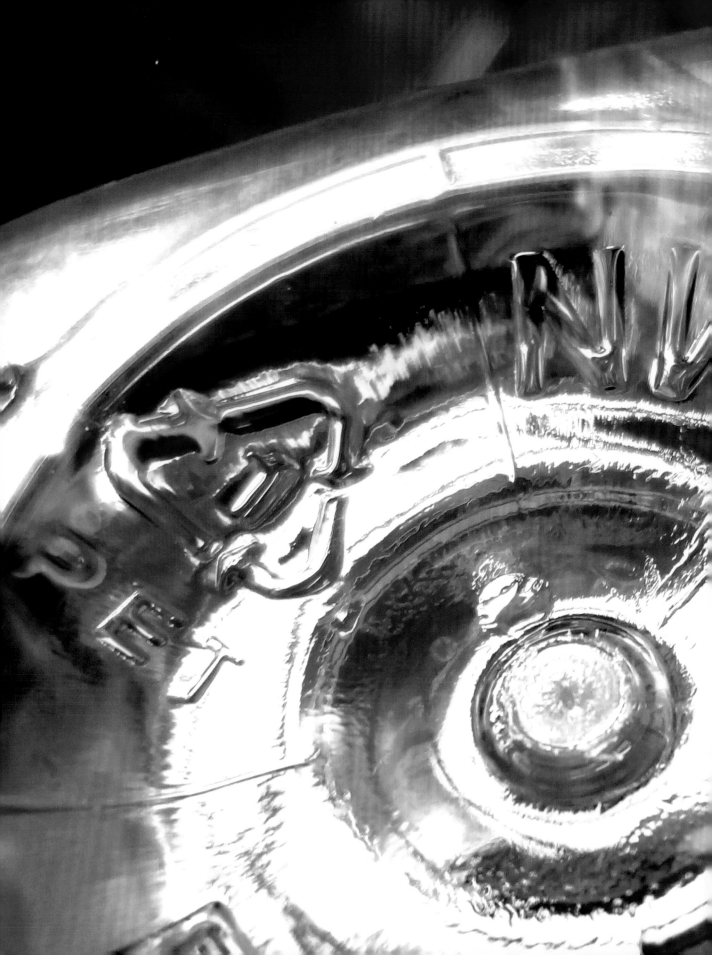

Offender:	Water and soft drink bottles can be made of PETE, a potentially carcinogenic chemical compound.
Alternative:	Use a home water filter instead of buying disposable bottles, and fill up your own reusable water bottle. Buy other beverages packaged in glass whenever possible.

Plastics Guide: what's behind the numbers on recycled plastics? None are proven to be safe, but numbers 1, 2, 4 & 5 are also not proven to be bad. When glass is unavailable, those are your best bets.

1 PETE

Agent 1, PETE:	Polyethylene Terephthalate
Alias:	Soft Drink Bottles, Water Bottles, Peanut Butter Jars, Cooking-Oil Bottles
Real Name:	Acetaldehyde

2 HDPE

Agent 2, HDPE:	High-Density Polyethylene
Alias:	Milk Jugs, Detergent Bottles, Plastic Bags, Yogurt Cups
Real Name:	BHT, Chimassorb 81, Irganox PS 800, Irganix 1076, Irganox 1010

3 V

Agent 3, PVC:	Polyvinyl Chloride
Alias:	Water Bottles, Salad-Dressing Bottles, Detergent Bottles, Cooking-Oil Bottles, Shampoo Bottles, Mouthwash Bottles, Meat Wrap, Babies' Pacifiers and Toys
Real Name:	Plasticizers (Lead, Cadmium, Mercury, Phthalates and Diethyl Hexyphosphate, a Carcinogen)

4 LDPE

Agent 4, LDPE:	Low-Density Polyethylene
Alias:	Produce Bags, Food-Storage Containers
Real Name:	BHT, Chimassorb 81, Irganox PS 800, Irganix 1076, Irganox 1010

5 PP

Agent 5, PP:	Polypropylene
Alias:	Bottle Caps, Drinking Straws
Real Name:	BHT, Chimassorb 81, Irganox PS 800, Irganix 1076, Irganox 1010

6 PS

Agent 6, PS:	Polystyrene
Alias:	Meat Trays, Foam Takeout Containers and Cups, Foam Packing Materials
Real Name:	Styrene

7 OTHER

Agent 7, Other Alias:	Laminated Food Containers, Water Bottles, Nylon
Real Name:	Unknown. Depends on plastics used. For example, polycarbonate leaches bisphenol-A.

Chapter Five

recipes

Now put on your prettiest apron to practice what you've learned with my original recipes for beautiful meals, prepared simply and lovingly to attract appetites, satisfy desires and nourish bodies.

shot glass salads

Before you start cooking, go to your liquor cabinet. This may sound promising to some and confusing to others, but just trust me. Take out a 3-ounce shot glass (or double shot) and bring it to the kitchen. Now you're ready to make salad!

My Shot Glass Salad recipes are easy guides to creating fresh salads that will keep your family asking for more healthy greens. Follow the brief step-by-step instructions to build a beautiful bowl of nutritious ingredients. When you make your masterpiece, write it in the blank boxes on the Your Favorites page to save the recipe for next time. Or try the My Favorite example on the next page to get started.

How the Shot Glass Salad was born:

When people ask me for a recipe, I normally tell them, "Oh, a little of this and some of that." I don't know how much I put in—I only know that it works. But after a few girlfriends begged me for measurements, I came up with this simple formula that any cook can customize to his or her desire. I discovered that the shot glasses sitting lonely in my cabinet were the perfect tools for portion control. They're easy, consistent measurements that anyone can succeed with. I find that people are often afraid to skip an ingredient or to improvise, but I made my recipes with freedom in mind, not fear. I want you to take my book as a guide to creating your own flavorful dishes.

Bon appétit!

tender greens

STEP 1: Choose two cups of your favorite greens per person

Tender Greens

Romaine Lettuce Spinach Mesclun Mixed Greens Arugula Watercress

STEP 2: Fill three shot glasses with any three items from the purple box

Vegetables

Green Beans	Fennel	Sprouts	Chickpeas	Mushrooms
Carrots	Radishes	Edamame	Peas	Asparagus
Tomatoes	Corn	Avocados	White Beans	Kidney Beans
Cucumbers	Black Beans	Beets	Red Onion	Bell Peppers
				Shallots

STEP 3: Add one shot glass each from the:
blue box,   red box   and brown box

Cheese
Blue: Roquefort,
   Stilton
Fresh: Goat, Feta
Hard: Parmigiano, Comte
Soft: Mozzarella

Accessories
Roasted Red Peppers,
Hearts of Palm,
Sun-Dried Tomatoes,
Artichoke Hearts, Capers
Olives: Green, Kalamata
Dried fruit: Raisins, Cranberries, Dates

Nuts
Almonds,
Walnuts,
Cashews, Pine Nuts,
Hazelnuts, Pecans
Seeds: Pumpkin, Flax

STEP 4: Choose a dressing and drizzle over tossed salad

Simple Vinaigrette
½ shot (or 1.5 ounces) olive oil
Juice of half a lemon
¼ teaspoon crushed garlic
1 teaspoon whole-grain mustard
Celtic sea salt
Freshly ground black pepper

or

Creamy Dressing
1 shot Greek yogurt
Juice of half a lemon
¼ teaspoon crushed garlic
1 tablespoon olive oil
Celtic sea salt
Freshly ground black pepper

STEP 5: Add any chopped garnish you like on top

Garnish

Scallions Parsley Basil Cilantro Mint Chives Tarragon

MY FAVORITE:
Tender Greens

Arugula

two cups

Arugula

one shot each

Fennel, Beets, and Shallots

one shot

Parmigiano Reggiano

one shot

Golden Raisins

one shot

Walnuts

Simple Vinaigrette

Tarragon

YOUR FAVORITES: Tender Greens

Write the ingredients you use on each line to make your own versions of my recipe.

Salad 1   _Salad 2_   _Salad 3_

STEP 1: Choose two cups of your favorite greens

two cups   two cups   two cups

_____   _____   _____

STEP 2: Fill three shot glasses with any three items from the purple box

one shot each   one shot each   one shot each

_____   _____   _____

_____   _____   _____

_____   _____   _____

STEP 3: Add one shot glass each from the:
blue box,   red box   and brown box

one shot   one shot   one shot

_____   _____   _____

one shot   one shot   one shot

_____   _____   _____

one shot   one shot   one shot

_____   _____   _____

STEP 4: Choose a dressing and drizzle over tossed salad

_____   _____   _____

STEP 5: Add any chopped garnish you like on top

_____   _____   _____

hearty greens

STEP 1: Choose two cups of your favorite greens per person

Hearty Greens

Green Cabbage   Kale   Red Cabbage   Swiss Chard   Napa Cabbage   Beet Greens

Make hearty greens softer by slicing thinly, adding simple vinaigrette and gently rubbing between palms. Cabbage can just be sliced.

Simple   or   Fancy

STEP 2: Fill three shot glasses with any three items from the purple box

Vegetables

Bell Peppers	Carrots
Tomatoes	Cucumbers
Fennel	Radishes
Green Beans	Sprouts
Edamame	Avocados
Beets	Chickpeas
White Beans	Corn
Red Onion	Mushrooms
Peas	Asparagus
Kidney Beans	Black Beans
Shallots	

STEP 2: Add one shot glass each from the blue box, red box and brown box

Cheese

Blue: Roquefort, Stilton
Fresh: Goat, Feta
Hard: Parmigiano, Comte
Soft: Mozzarella

Accessories
Roasted Red Peppers, Capers,
Artichoke Hearts, Olives,
Sun-Dried Tomatoes, Hearts of Palm
Dried fruit: Raisins, Cranberries, Dates

Nuts
Almonds, Pecans, Walnuts,
Cashews, Pine Nuts, Hazelnuts
Seeds: Pumpkin, Flax

STEP 3: Add Simple Vinaigrette and toss the salad

Simple Vinaigrette

½ shot (or 1.5 ounces) olive oil
Juice of half a lemon
¼ teaspoon crushed garlic
1 teaspoon whole-grain mustard
Celtic sea salt
Freshly ground black pepper

STEP 3: Add Creamy Dressing and toss the salad

Creamy Dressing

1 shot Greek yogurt
Juice of half a lemon
¼ teaspoon crushed garlic
1 tablespoon olive oil
Celtic sea salt
Freshly ground black pepper

STEP 4: Add any chopped garnish you like on top

Garnish

Scallions   Parsley   Basil   Cilantro   Mint   Chives   Tarragon

MY FAVORITE:
Hearty Greens

Simple

two cups	Red Cabbage

one shot each	Radishes, Grape Tomatoes, and Red Onion
	Simple Vinaigrette
	Mint

Fancy

two cups	Kale

one shot	Comte

one shot	Kalamata Olives

one shot	Toasted Pine Nuts
	Creamy Dressing
	Parsley

YOUR FAVORITES: Hearty Greens

Write the ingredients you use on each line to make your own versions of my recipe.

Simple Salad 1   Simple Salad 2   Simple Salad 3

STEP 1: Choose two cups of your favorite greens

two cups	two cups	two cups
_____	_____	_____

STEP 2: Fill three shot glasses with any three items from the purple box

one shot each	one shot each	one shot each
_____	_____	_____
_____	_____	_____

STEP 3: Add Simple Vinaigrette and toss the salad

Simple Vinaigrette	Simple Vinaigrette	Simple Vinaigrette

STEP 4: Add any chopped garnish you like on top

_____	_____	_____

Fancy Salad 1   Fancy Salad 2   Fancy Salad 3

STEP 1: Choose two cups of your favorite greens

two cups	two cups	two cups
_____	_____	_____

STEP 2: Add one shot glass each from the:
blue box,   **red box**   **and brown box**

one shot	one shot	one shot
one shot	one shot	one shot
one shot	one shot	one shot

STEP 3: Add Creamy Dressing and toss the salad

Creamy Dressing	Creamy Dressing	Creamy Dressing

STEP 4: Add any chopped garnish you like on top

_____	_____	_____

grains & legumes

STEP 1: Choose a quarter-cup of any grains or legumes per person

Grains

Brown Rice, Barley, Bulgur Wheat, Quinoa, Kamut, Wheat Berries
Cook, salt, drain, cool.

Legumes

Beans: Black, Kidney, Pinto, Garbanzo, White
Lentils: Green, Black
Cooked or canned.

STEP 2: Choose two cups of your favorite greens

Tender Greens

Romaine Lettuce   Spinach   Mesclun Mixed Greens   Arugula   Watercress

STEP 3: Fill three shot glasses with any three items from the purple box

Vegetables

Green Beans	Fennel	Sprouts	Chickpeas	Mushrooms
Carrots	Radishes	Edamame	Peas	Asparagus
Tomatoes	Corn	Avocados	White Beans	Kidney Beans
Cucumbers	Black Beans	Beets	Red Onion	Bell Peppers
				Shallots

STEP 4: Add one shot glass each from the:
blue box,   red box   and brown box

Cheese

Blue: Roquefort, Stilton
Fresh: Goat, Feta
Hard: Parmigiano, Comte
Soft: Mozzarella

Accessories

Roasted Red Peppers, Hearts of Palm, Sun-Dried Tomatoes, Artichoke Hearts, Capers
Olives: Green, Kalamata
Dried fruit: Raisins, Cranberries, Dates

Nuts

Almonds, Walnuts, Cashews, Pine Nuts, Hazelnuts, Pecans
Seeds: Pumpkin, Flax

STEP 5: Choose a dressing and drizzle over tossed salad

Simple Vinaigrette

½ shot (or 1.5 ounces) olive oil
Juice of half a lemon
¼ teaspoon crushed garlic
1 teaspoon whole-grain mustard
Celtic sea salt
Freshly ground black pepper

or

Creamy Dressing

1 shot Greek yogurt
Juice of half a lemon
¼ teaspoon crushed garlic
1 tablespoon olive oil
Celtic sea salt
Freshly ground black pepper

STEP 6: Add any chopped garnish you like on top

Garnish

Scallions   Parsley   Basil   Cilantro   Mint   Chives   Tarragon

MY FAVORITE:
Grains & Legumes

White Beans

quarter-cup

White Beans

two cups

Arugula

one shot each

Tomato, Asparagus, and
Yellow Peppers

one shot

Blue Cheese

one shot

Capers

one shot

Walnuts

Creamy Dressing

Chives

YOUR FAVORITES: Grains & Legumes

Write the ingredients you use on each line to make your own versions of my recipe.

Salad 1   *Salad 2*   *Salad 3*

STEP 1: Choose a quarter-cup of any grains or legumes per person

quarter-cup   quarter-cup   quarter-cup

_____   _____   _____

STEP 2: Choose two cups of your favorite greens

two cups   two cups   two cups

_____   _____   _____

STEP 3: Fill three shot glasses with any three items from the purple box

one shot each   one shot each   one shot each

_____   _____   _____

_____   _____   _____

_____   _____   _____

STEP 4: Add one shot glass each from the:
blue box,   ### red box   ### and brown box

one shot   one shot   one shot

_____   _____   _____

one shot   one shot   one shot

_____   _____   _____

one shot   one shot   one shot

_____   _____   _____

STEP 5: Choose a dressing and drizzle over tossed salad

_____   _____   _____

STEP 6: Add any chopped garnish you like on top

_____   _____   _____

roasted vegetables

STEP 1: Choose one cup of vegetables, squash or potatoes per person

Hearty Vegetables
Artichokes, Beets,
Asparagus, Brussels Sprouts

Roast in oven, cool and chop.

Squash & Potatoes
Squash: Acorn, Butternut, Pumpkin
Potatoes: White, Sweet

Roast whole in oven, cool and cube.

STEP 2: Choose two cups of your favorite greens

Tender Greens
Romaine Lettuce   Spinach   Mesclun Mixed Greens   Arugula   Watercress

STEP 3: Fill three shot glasses with any three items from the purple box

Vegetables

Green Beans	Fennel	Sprouts	Chickpeas	Mushrooms
Carrots	Radishes	Edamame	Peas	Asparagus
Tomatoes	Corn	Avocados	White Beans	Kidney Beans
Cucumbers	Black Beans	Beets	Red Onion	Bell Peppers
				Shallots

STEP 4: Add one shot glass each from the:
blue box,   red box   and brown box

Cheese
Blue: Roquefort,
    Stilton
Fresh: Goat, Feta
Hard: Parmigiano, Comte
Soft: Mozzarella

Accessories
Roasted Red Peppers,
Hearts of Palm,
Sun-Dried Tomatoes,
Artichoke Hearts, Capers
Olives: Green, Kalamata
Dried fruit: Raisins, Cranberries, Dates

Nuts
Almonds,
Walnuts,
Cashews, Pine Nuts,
Hazelnuts, Pecans
Seeds: Pumpkin, Flax

STEP 5: Choose a dressing and drizzle over tossed salad

Simple Vinaigrette
½ shot (or 1.5 ounces) olive oil
Juice of half a lemon
¼ teaspoon crushed garlic
1 teaspoon whole-grain mustard
Celtic sea salt
Freshly ground black pepper

    or

Creamy Dressing
1 shot Greek yogurt
Juice of half a lemon
¼ teaspoon crushed garlic
1 tablespoon olive oil
Celtic sea salt
Freshly ground black pepper

STEP 6: Add any chopped garnish you like on top

Garnish
Scallions   Parsley   Basil   Cilantro   Mint   Chives   Tarragon

MY FAVORITE:
Roasted Vegetables

Acorn Squash

one cup

Acorn Squash

one cup

Spinach

one shot each

Beets, Fennel, and Red Onion

one shot

Goat Cheese

one shot

Artichoke Hearts

one shot

Pumpkin Seeds

Simple Vinaigrette

Chives

YOUR FAVORITES: Roasted Vegetables

Write the ingredients you use on each line to make your own versions of my recipe.

Salad 1	*Salad 2*	*Salad 3*

STEP 1: Choose one cup of vegetables, squash or potatoes per person

one cup	one cup	one cup
_____	_____	_____

STEP 2: Choose two cups of your favorite greens

two cups	two cups	two cups
_____	_____	_____

STEP 3: Fill three shot glasses with any three items from the purple box

one shot each	one shot each	one shot each
_____	_____	_____
_____	_____	_____
_____	_____	_____

STEP 4: Add one shot glass each from the:
    blue box,   **red box**   **and brown box**

one shot	one shot	one shot
_____	_____	_____
one shot	one shot	one shot
_____	_____	_____
one shot	one shot	one shot
_____	_____	_____

STEP 5: Choose a dressing and drizzle over tossed salad

_____	_____	_____

STEP 6: Add any chopped garnish you like on top

_____	_____	_____

soups

These recipes have endless mouthwatering possibilities, and just like the Shot Glass Salads, they're merely patterns to play with. I've provided a few easy guidelines for making soup out of whatever you have on hand. The next time you're cuddled under a blanket and need a hot meal fast, try one of these recipes with almost anything you have in your vegetable drawer or pantry. No need to go to the store; just get up and get cooking!

basic vegetable stock

You can use this delicious homemade stock as the base of my soup recipes or in place of water in many other recipes. Just throw some leftover vegetables – even peels – into a pot of water, forget about it for a couple of hours and presto: you made your own stock!

1 onion
3 large carrots, unpeeled
2 whole cloves garlic
Any leftover raw vegetables or peels
5 whole peppercorns
1 bay leaf
1 sprig each fresh rosemary and thyme (or a pinch of dry)
2 teaspoons sea salt

Clean vegetables and chop roughly into 2-inch pieces. Throw into a large, tall soup pot with herbs and fill with 5 liters of cold filtered water. Cover and bring to a boil; then reduce heat to low and simmer partly covered for 2 hours. Add 2 teaspoons salt – you can always add more later when you use the stock in a recipe. Strain through a fine sieve and let cool before storing in glass jars.

Keeps two weeks in the fridge or two months in the freezer.

tender greens

1. Wash and chop 4 cups of your favorite tender greens.

   Romaine Lettuce   Spinach   Watercress   Arugula

   Set aside to dry.

2. Heat 2 tablespoons olive oil over medium heat in a large pot.
3. Sauté one small leek (about 1 cup, thinly sliced) for one minute.
4. Cook one small potato (about 1 cup, peeled and cubed) about five more minutes.

Optional
Add one clove crushed garlic and one diced carrot and sauté another minute.
You can also substitute one diced parsnip or white yam for the potato.

5. Pour 4 cups water or homemade vegetable stock into pot and bring to a boil.

6. Add your favorite herbs and seasonings to taste.

Black pepper	Ground Coriander	Mint
Cayenne Pepper	Freshly Grated Ginger	Parsley
Paprika	Basil	Cilantro
Tarragon	Thyme	

7. Simmer over low heat about 20 minutes, until vegetables are tender.

8. Add salt and blend tender greens into soup with a hand blender until smooth.

9. Enjoy each bowl of soup with your favorite toppings.

Squeeze of Lemon Juice	Shaved Parmesan Cheese
Sliced Scallions	Spoonful of Greek Yogurt
Drizzle of Balsamic Vinegar	Chopped Fresh Herbs

MY FAVORITE:
Tender Greens

Fresh Spinach

four cups

Spinach

two tablespoons

Olive Oil

one cup

Sliced Leeks

one cup

Cubed Potatoes

one clove

Crushed Garlic

four cups

Vegetable Stock

Salt, Black Pepper

Lemon

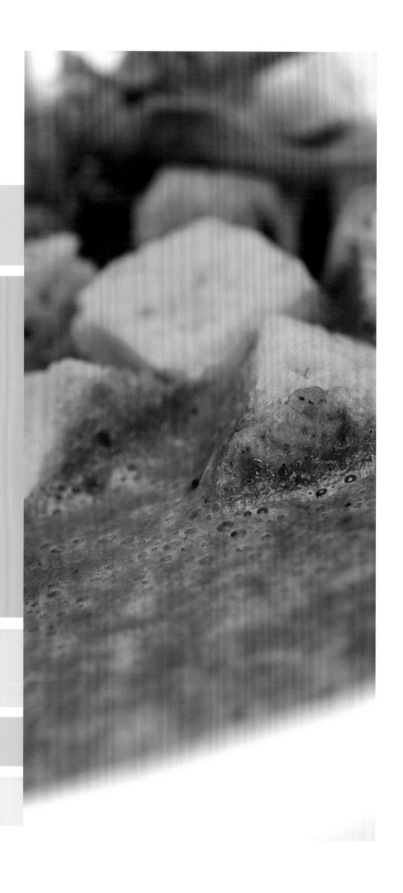

Use spinach for spotless skin...

Heat a large handful of dry, clean spinach leaves in a cup of milk over low heat until the leaves wilt

Place a layer of warm leaves over your face and lie down for a half-hour

Wash your face with warm water

...good for thin skin and fine lines, gives an even tone and glowing complexion.

Mix a large handful of dry, clean spinach leaves in a blender with one egg yolk

Spread mixture on your face and leave for a half-hour

Wash your face with warm water

...good for very dry skin, repairs sun damage and smooths complexion.

Heat a large handful of dry, clean spinach leaves in a cup of water over low heat until the leaves wilt

Place a layer of warm leaves over your face and lie down for a half-hour

Wash your face with warm water

...good for lightening dark spots and repairing sun damage.

Pamper your hair with olive oil...

Mix equal parts olive oil, castor oil and coconut oil

Add one clove crushed garlic and mix well

Massage oil into hair and leave it for three hours

Meanwhile, make a strong infusion of chamomile and fresh lemon juice

Wash hair in the chamomile-lemon water to remove garlic scent

Wash again normally with your favorite shampoo

...strengthens hair and adds lustrous shine.

vegetable

1. Wash and chop 2 cups of your favorite vegetable.

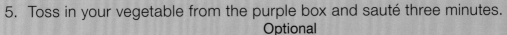

| Asparagus | Broccoli | Broccolini | Cabbage | Carrot | |
| Cauliflower | Kale | Mushroom | Pea | Potato | Tomato |

2. Heat 2 tablespoons olive oil over medium heat in a large pot.
3. Sauté one small leek (about 1 cup, thinly sliced) for one minute.
4. Cook one small potato (about 1 cup, peeled and cubed) about five more minutes.
5. Toss in your vegetable from the purple box and sauté three minutes.

Optional

Add one clove crushed garlic and one diced carrot and sauté another minute.
You can also substitute one diced parsnip or white yam for the potato.

6. Pour 3 cups water and 3 cups homemade vegetable stock into pot; bring to a boil.

7. Add your favorite herbs and seasonings to taste.

Black Pepper	Ground Coriander	Mint
Cayenne Pepper	Freshly Grated Ginger	Parsley
Paprika	Basil	Cilantro
Tarragon	Thyme	Rosemary
		Sage

8. Simmer over low heat about 20 minutes, until vegetables are tender.

9. Add salt and blend soup with a hand blender to the consistency you like; blend a short time to leave it slightly chunky or blend longer for a smooth soup.

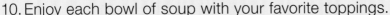

10. Enjoy each bowl of soup with your favorite toppings.

Squeeze of Lemon Juice	Shaved Parmesan Cheese
Sliced Scallions	Spoonful of Greek Yogurt
Drizzle of Balsamic Vinegar	Chopped Fresh Herbs

MY FAVORITE:
Vegetable

Creamy Cauliflower

two cups

Cauliflower

two tablespoons

Olive Oil

one cup

Sliced Leeks

one cup

Cubed Potatoes

three cups each

Water, Vegetable Stock

Salt, Thyme, Rosemary

Parmesan

Soften skin with sesame oil…

    Spread sesame oil on your lips and any dry, rough skin

    Wash skin with soap and warm water

…good for softening rough spots and smoothing the skin.

Take the tomato treatment…

    Squeeze the juice out of several over-ripe tomatoes

    Wash your face with the juice and leave it for a half-hour

    Wash skin with warm water

…gently exfoliates, reduces the size of large pores and tightens skin.

    Peel one tomato and blend with a spoonful each of lemon juice and yogurt

    Spread on your face and leave it for fifteen minutes

    Wash skin with warm water

…good for acne-prone skin.

Elevate and exfoliate with radishes…

    Grate a radish and mix with the juice of one lemon

    Place mixture in a warm spot and leave it for 48 hours

    Drain the excess liquid from the soaked radish

    Spread the radish on your face and leave it for an hour

    Wash skin with soap and warm water

…lightens dark spots, exfoliates, evens tone and lifts facial skin.

    Juice a bunch of red radishes and mix with an equal amount of castor oil

    Massage through hair roots and scalp

    Leave overnight, protecting your pillow with a small towel

    Wash hair the next morning normally with your favorite shampoo

…good for thinning hair or hair loss.

legumes

1. Soak 1 cup of your favorite beans overnight: **black, white, pinto, garbanzo**
-OR-
1. Rinse 1 cup of your favorite lentils: **black, green, red**
2. Drain legumes and cook for three-quarters of the recommended time or until still slightly firm in the center – do not salt the water or the legumes will be tough. (**Note: Red lentils need no pre-cooking – skip ahead to step 4.**)
3. Drain the partially cooked legumes and set aside.

4. Heat 2 tablespoons olive oil over medium heat in a large pot.
5. Sauté one small leek (about 1 cup, thinly sliced) for one minute.
6. Cook one small potato (about 1 cup, peeled and cubed) about five more minutes.

Optional
Add one clove crushed garlic and one diced carrot and sauté another minute.
You can also substitute one diced parsnip or white yam for the potato.

If you're using lentils:
7. Pour 4 cups water or homemade vegetable stock into pot and bring to a boil.
8. Toss in your partially cooked lentils from the black box.

If you're using beans:
7. Pour 4 cups water into pot and bring to a boil. Add 1 cup pureed tomatoes (fresh in season or canned).
8. Toss in your partially cooked beans from the black box.

9. Add your favorite herbs and seasonings to taste.

Black Pepper	Ground Coriander	Marjoram
Cayenne Pepper	Ground Cumin	Thyme
Paprika	Bay Leaf	Rosemary
		Sage

10. Simmer over low heat about 30 minutes, until legumes are tender.
11. Add salt. Lentil soup can be made smooth with a hand blender or left as it is.

12. Serve each bowl of soup with a cooked grain of your choice on the side.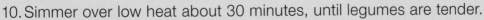
Brown Rice   Barley   Bulgur Wheat   Quinoa   Wheat Berries   Kamut

MY FAVORITE:
Legumes

Spiced Lentil

one cup

Green Lentils

two tablespoons

Olive Oil

one cup

Sliced Leeks, Cubed Potatoes

one clove

Crushed Garlic

one

Diced Carrot

four cups

Vegetable Stock

Salt, Ground Cumin

Greek Yogurt

Beauty Tips

Treat puffy eyes with potatoes…

    Slice a potato thinly

    Place fresh slices around eye area, especially under eyes

    Leave them for at least a half-hour

    Wash skin around eyes gently with warm water

…good for curing puffy, tired eyes.

Revive with apple cider vinegar…

    Mix 2 tablespoons apple cider vinegar with a cup of water

    Drink the mixture before breakfast every morning

    Those with sensitive stomachs should eat before drinking the mixture

…good for burning fat, alleviates joint pain from arthritis.

Lighten up with lemon…

    Mix lemon juice and olive oil in equal amounts

    Spread a thin layer on your face and leave for two hours

    Wash skin thoroughly with soap and warm water

    Do this only before bed at nighttime; wash face well before going in the sun

…good for wrinkles, lightens dark spots, exfoliates; best for oily skin, not dry skin.

Grow stronger with onion…

    Dice 2 large onions and boil in 1 quart water for ten minutes

    Drain liquid and let cool, and then add a teaspoon of rosewater

    Massage liquid into your hair roots and scalp for a half-hour

    Boil water and let steam open your pores while you massage

    Leave in your hair for two hours

    Wash hair normally with your favorite shampoo

…strengthens root follicles, promotes hair growth and combats hair loss or thinning.

main courses

Many of these wonderfully simple recipes are staples from my family home and some are even centuries old! They nurtured us and will encourage your loved ones to savor their health at every meal.

bulgur wheat and chickpea pilaf

2 tablespoons extra-virgin olive oil
1 medium onion
2 cups coarse bulgur wheat (often labeled "#3: coarse")
1 cup dry chickpeas, soaked 24 hours and boiled until tender
   (rinse and drain if using canned)
3 cups chicken stock, vegetable stock or water
Sea salt or Himalayan salt
Black pepper

Rinse and drain bulgur wheat and chickpeas separately; set aside. Peel and dice onion finely. Place a medium pot on the stove over medium heat. Once pot is hot, add olive oil and reduce heat to medium-low. Sauté onion until translucent, about four minutes. Add bulgur wheat, then chickpeas and stir to combine evenly.

Pour in your chosen liquid, add seasonings to taste and cover the pot, turning the heat up to medium-high. When the liquid boils, turn the heat down to low and simmer, covered, until the bulgur wheat is tender and all the liquid has been absorbed.

Yara's Memories

In the coastal mountains, we make this ancient dish as the customary companion of meat sacrificed for a holiday or special occasion. Cauldrons bubble over wood fires until the lamb or chicken meat falls off the bone. The resulting stock is always put to good use. It simmers with bulgur and chickpeas until they become a light, fluffy pilaf. You can make it with vegetable stock and serve it as a flavorful alternative to rice with any of my vegetarian dishes, such as okra or green beans.

rice and lentil pilaf

1 cup brown rice, soaked four hours and drained
1 cup green lentils
3 ½ cups chicken stock, vegetable stock or water
4 tablespoons extra-virgin olive oil
1 medium onion
Sea salt or Himalayan salt
Black pepper

Rinse and drain lentils; pour into medium pot. Add chosen liquid and place covered pot on the stove over high heat. When the liquid boils, turn the heat down to low and simmer, covered, until the lentils are almost tender, or al dente. Add drained brown rice and seasonings to taste, cover pot and continue simmering until rice is tender and all the liquid has been absorbed.

Meanwhile, peel the onion and slice thinly lengthwise from root to end. Heat olive oil on medium-high heat in a large pan. Add onion and reduce heat to medium-low so that it slowly caramelizes, about ten minutes. While the oil is still hot and just before serving, pour the entire contents of the pan evenly over top of the finished pilaf to cover with caramelized onions.

Yara's Memories

Wise wives have been fueling hard-working farmers with rice and lentil pilaf for centuries because the two main ingredients make an energy-rich complete protein that's available and affordable. They welcome the men into the house with the scent of caramelized onions in the air (an appetizing trick I love to use when I want to tempt the appetites of my dinner guests). These ordinary people were extraordinarily healthy and fit and often outlived the wealthy who dined extravagantly. Now, the popular perception of these "poor people's foods" has changed and everyone enjoys this standard dish.

tomato bulgur wheat pilaf

2 tablespoons extra-virgin olive oil
1 medium onion
1 medium bell pepper of your favorite color (or mix colors!)
1 cup coarse bulgur wheat (often labeled "#3: coarse")
1 cup pureed fresh tomatoes (canned may be substituted)
1 tablespoon tomato paste
½ cup liquid of your choice: chicken stock, vegetable stock or water
Sea salt or Himalayan salt
Black pepper

Rinse and drain bulgur wheat; set aside. Peel onion. Dice onion and bell pepper finely. Place a medium pot on the stove over medium heat. Once pot is hot, add olive oil and reduce heat to medium-low. Sauté onion until almost translucent, about two minutes. Add diced bell pepper to onion and continue cooking about two minutes to soften. Add bulgur wheat and stir to combine evenly.

Pour in your chosen liquid, tomato puree and tomato paste, add seasonings to taste and cover the pot, turning the heat up to medium-high. When the liquid boils, turn the heat down to low and simmer, covered, until the bulgur wheat is tender and all the liquid has been absorbed.

Yara's Memories

Our neighbor was the absolute master of Tomato Bulgur Wheat Pilaf. I don't know how she did it, but every time she had a dinner party, this upstaged all the other foods on the table. My version is delicious, and someday I'll learn to make hers, as well.

upside-down eggplant and rice

2 cups long-grain rice of your choice: if brown soak four hours, if white soak two hours
2 medium eggplants
2 medium onions
3 ½ to 4 cups chicken stock, vegetable stock or water
Sea salt or Himalayan salt
Pinch of each seasoning: black pepper, cumin, coriander, allspice, cinnamon and turmeric
½ cup pine nuts
¼ cup sliced almonds

Preheat oven to 375 degrees Fahrenheit and line baking sheet with natural parchment paper. Peel eggplant and cut lengthwise from stem to end in about quarter-inch-thick slices. Place eggplant slices in a single layer on the baking sheet, using two sheets if necessary. Bake until edges begin to brown and flesh is tender, about fifteen minutes. Set eggplant aside.

Pour nuts in a single layer on a baking sheet. Roast nuts in the oven until golden brown, about five minutes (watch carefully, as they burn quickly!). Set aside to cool. Peel onions and slice thinly lengthwise from root to end. Heat olive oil in a large pan, add onions and sauté until translucent, about four minutes; set aside.

In a large pot, place all roasted eggplant slices on bottom to form an even layer. Next, make a layer of sautéed onions over the eggplant. Drain the rice and add to the pot to form the third and final layer.

Separately, pour chosen liquid into a large mixing bowl and add all seasonings. Combine with a whisk until there are no lumps of spices. Pour liquid over rice in the large pot, cover tightly and place pot on the stove over high heat. When the liquid boils, turn the heat down to low and simmer, covered, until the rice is tender. Remove pot from heat, but keep covered an additional ten minutes to let the layers settle.

Just before serving, remove the cover, place a large serving dish face-down over the pot and very carefully flip the contents onto the dish. Put the whole thing down on your kitchen counter and slowly lift the pot straight up. The pilaf should appear in upside-down layers: eggplant on top, then onions and rice on bottom. Serve topped with roasted almond slices and pine nuts.

Beauty Tips

Purify your pores with parsley…

Wash a bundle of parsley

Boil the bundle in 2 cups of water for five minutes

Drain the water into a bowl and set aside until just warm

Wash your face with the parsley water, rubbing well, for fifteen minutes

…good for dark circles, puffy eyes, clears skin of blemishes and blackheads.

Wash a bundle of parsley

Blend the bundle with a little water until a smooth paste forms

Spread parsley paste over entire face, focusing on areas with blackheads

Bring a pot of water to boil, lean over and steam your face for five minutes

Massage face for an additional five minutes while warm

Wash your face with warm water

…clears skin of blemishes and removes blackheads.

stuffed cabbage leaves and peppers

1 medium head green cabbage
2 medium bell peppers (choose your favorite color)
1 cup short-grain rice, soaked two hours and drained
2 medium onions
2 cups chopped mushrooms (choose your favorite type or mix them)
2 tablespoons extra-virgin olive oil
1½ cups chicken stock, vegetable stock or water
½ cup pureed fresh tomatoes (canned may be substituted)
Sea salt or Himalayan salt
Pinch of each seasoning: black pepper, cumin, coriander, allspice, cinnamon and dried mint

Preheat oven to 350 degrees Fahrenheit. Bring a large pot of water to a boil. Meanwhile, remove the core from the cabbage and carefully peel off the largest 10 leaves. Rinse and cut out the thick rib from each leaf. Blanch leaves in boiling water until tender, about five minutes, and then shock in ice water to cool; drain well. Rinse peppers and remove stems, ribs and seeds. Set vegetables aside.

Peel and dice onion finely. Heat olive oil on medium heat in a small pot. Add onion and reduce heat to medium-low, sauté two minutes, and then add chopped mushrooms and continue cooking about two minutes. Add rice, 1 cup of your chosen liquid and all seasonings, stirring well to combine. Turn up to high heat until the liquid boils, and then turn the heat down to low and simmer, covered, until the rice is almost tender, or al dente.

Lay cabbage leaves out on a clean kitchen counter or cutting board. Place a tablespoon of the rice mixture at the base of each leaf, folding each side inward toward the center. Then roll the leaf from base to tip and place with the crease facing down in a deep casserole dish. Repeat until all 10 leaves are filled. Spoon the remaining rice mixture into the two bell peppers, leaving a half-inch of empty space at the top for the rice to expand. Set the peppers in the casserole dish.

In a small bowl, whisk together the remaining ½ cup liquid and ½ cup tomato puree with a pinch of salt. Pour over the casserole dish and cover tightly with aluminum foil. Bake for 20 to 30 minutes or until rice is tender and vegetables are fully cooked.

Yara's Memories

Most cultures have a tradition of stuffing vegetables. It's always been a nutritious way to stretch your food budget—use a small amount of meat and a few handfuls of rice to fill whatever produce is abundant in your area of the world. In Syria we stuff all kinds of ingredients, from eggplant to zucchini and grape leaves to potatoes. My vegetarian recipe for stuffed cabbage leaves and peppers is especially good for you and one of my favorites.

Beauty Tips

Nourish your skin with carrots…
- Wash 2 carrots and grate them
- Mix 1 tablespoon raw honey into the grated carrots
- Spread on your face and leave it for twenty minutes
- Wash your face with warm water

…good for cellular nutrition of the skin.

Firm your face with yogurt…
- Blend one soft-boiled potato with ½ cup yogurt and the juice of half a lemon
- Spread on your face and leave it for a half-hour
- Wash your face thoroughly with warm water

…good for lightening dark spots and firming the skin.

crusted snapper

Whole red snapper or your favorite fresh fish, cleaned by your fishmonger
4 tablespoons extra-virgin olive oil
½ cup whole wheat bread crumbs
½ cup whole wheat flour
½ cup instant potato flakes
Sea salt or Himalayan salt
Black pepper
Lemon slices
Fresh parsley sprigs

Preheat oven to 325 degrees Fahrenheit. Mix bread crumbs, flour and potato flakes together in a shallow dish. Season fish with salt and pepper. Drizzle a tablespoon of olive oil over each side of the fish and rub to coat. Dip one side of the fish in bread-crumb mixture and pat to be sure the crust sticks well.

Heat remaining olive oil on medium-high in a large cast-iron sauté pan (or other oven-safe pan). Add fish with the crust side down and sauté four minutes to brown. Flip fish carefully with a spatula and continue cooking three minutes. Place fish in the oven for five minutes to cook through. Serve with lemons and parsley for garnish.

Yara's Memories

I love to cook, but sometimes I like to hang up my apron and appreciate a good meal in a restaurant. On one of those occasions, I ordered a whole red snapper caught locally and prepared in a buttery crust. I loved the crunchy texture of the outside paired with the soft white fish on the inside but couldn't finish the fabulous dish because it was so rich. Over the next week I tortured my honey with more seafood dinners than anyone could or should eat—I knew I could make that recipe more healthful, and I experimented until I succeeded. It's quick to prepare, and you can use the same method with any type of fish. I hope you enjoy this slightly indulgent, wholly nutritious meal as much as I do!

side dishes

My vegetarian side dishes pair perfectly with almost any main course, including meat. Or you may like them so much that you'll want to make a meal of them like we do in my culture. Just pick a pilaf from the first few main courses and serve it with one of the following aromatic recipes for an incredible exotic dinner.

potatoes with cilantro

3 tablespoons extra-virgin olive oil
2 medium potatoes
3 cloves garlic
½ cup fresh cilantro
Juice of half a lemon
Sea salt or Himalayan salt
Black pepper

Peel and chop potatoes in 1-inch cubes, soak in cold water, and set aside. Chop cilantro leaves roughly and peel and mince garlic. Drain potatoes well.

Heat olive oil on medium-high in a large sauté pan. Add potatoes and sauté two minutes; cover pan and continue cooking until tender, about ten minutes. Uncover pan, add minced garlic and sauté another minute. Squeeze juice of lemon half over potatoes, add cilantro and season to taste with salt and pepper. Serve with Crusted Snapper.

Yara's Memories

I don't know why, but everyone seems to agree on one thing: potatoes are fabulous! Sauteed, steamed, baked, fried—they all taste great. I tend toward the healthy side of cooking, so I prefer my potatoes lightly sautéed with a kick of seasoning. As I'd walk in the door of my family's home, the smell of cilantro toasting in the pan hinted to me from the doorway that lunch would be tasty, and that scent still gets my appetite going. You'll love this wholesome family recipe and the uncommon flavors.

okra

3 tablespoons extra-virgin olive oil
1 medium onion
5 cloves garlic
2 cups okra (frozen or fresh recommended)
1 cup pureed fresh tomatoes (canned may be substituted)
1 tablespoon tomato paste
½ cup liquid of your choice: chicken stock, vegetable stock or water
Sea salt or Himalayan salt
Coriander

Peel and chop both onion and garlic roughly; set aside. Heat olive oil on medium-high in a large sauté pan. Add onion and reduce heat to medium-low, sauté until almost translucent, about two minutes. Add garlic to pan and sauté another minute. Add okra and continue cooking about five minutes to brown the okra slightly.

Add salt and coriander to the pan and stir well for one minute. Pour in tomato sauce, tomato paste, and your chosen liquid just to cover okra. Turn up the heat and bring liquid to a boil; reduce and simmer, partly covered, until okra is tender, about ten minutes. Serve with rice on the side.

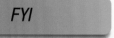

FYI

Don't ignore okra! Instead of throwing it into a gumbo, make okra the star of your meal. I keep it light and simple, not camouflaged in a fried coating. The tomatoes, garlic and coriander in this recipe are perfect companions and support the okra without upstaging it. Whether you've had a bad okra experience or you already love it, my rendition will show you the mouthwatering appeal of okra.

The secret to success is proper preparation. If you have a local farmers' market, get your okra fresh, wash it and simply cut off the tip of the stem (less than a quarter of an inch, just to remove any part that has dried or hardened after harvest). In a pinch, organic frozen okra can be found at almost any grocery store.

baba ghanoush

1 large eggplant
1 small clove garlic
2 teaspoons sesame tahini
1 tablespoon yogurt
Squeeze of fresh lemon juice
Sea salt or Himalayan salt
1 tablespoon extra-virgin olive oil
Fresh mint leaves or parsley for garnish

Preheat oven to 400 degrees Fahrenheit. Place eggplant on a baking sheet and poke several times with a small knife to allow steam to escape. Roast eggplant in the oven for thirty minutes or until skin looks disheveled and flesh caves under slight pressure from a knife. Remove from oven and let rest twenty minutes. Carefully slice open the roasted eggplant and allow all steam to escape before handling.

For best results and cleanest fingernails, wear a pair of disposable gloves when handling the eggplant. Cut off the stem end and pull flesh from the skin (it should peel away easily). Discard skin and put eggplant flesh on a cutting board. Chop with a large knife until very fine. Alternatively, you can break down the roasted eggplant flesh in a food processor by pulsing until pieces are small but not liquefied.

Place eggplant in a medium mixing bowl. Add crushed garlic, tahini, yogurt, lemon juice and salt to taste, mixing well. Place in a shallow dish, drizzle with olive oil, and garnish with fresh mint or parsley. Serve as a spread or a dip with pita bread and raw vegetables.

Yara's Memories

Baba Ghanoush has claimed its place on the Syrian and Lebanese table of traditional mezze (appetizers). No ethnic feast is complete without it. The original version calls for the eggplant to be charred in a blistering tannour oven, and I've been lucky enough to savor the smoky spread. We have many dishes in our cuisine that feature eggplant; we cook it with rice, we roast it, we stuff it and we bake it. This recipe pairs eggplant with nutritious, creamy sesame tahini, which is full of B vitamins, calcium and essential fatty acids.

green beans in tomato sauce

3 tablespoons extra-virgin olive oil
1 medium onion
5 cloves garlic
2 cups fresh green beans (frozen may be substituted)
1 cup pureed fresh tomatoes (canned may be substituted)
1 cup chicken stock, vegetable stock or water
Sea salt or Himalayan salt
Coriander

Peel and chop both onion and garlic roughly; set aside. Cut green beans into 1-inch pieces; set aside. Heat olive oil on medium-high in a large sauté pan. Add onion and reduce heat to medium-low; sauté until almost translucent, about two minutes. Add garlic to pan and sauté another minute. Add green beans and continue cooking about five minutes.

Add salt and coriander to the pan and stir well for one minute. Pour in tomato sauce and your chosen liquid just to cover beans. Turn up the heat and bring liquid to a boil; reduce and simmer, partly covered, until beans are tender and sauce has thickened slightly, about thirty minutes. Serve with rice on the side.

Does this vegetable look familiar? The last time you saw it might have been while you were downing a few slices of roasted turkey, cornbread stuffing, sweet potato casserole and pumpkin pie, remember? It was that little green object peeking out from under a mound of fried onions somewhere behind the untouched bowl of salad at Thanksgiving dinner. Or maybe you know these long, thin beans from beneath the shadow of your 14-ounce filet at your favorite high-end steakhouse. In either case, I want to introduce you to one of the most popular vegetables in my culture: the green bean. It's amazing what wonderful variations come from a simple twist in the recipe, and because I'm all about giving you the means to create multiple meals from one idea, I'll give you two takes on the green bean theme.

In summer, I use the ripe tomatoes that are a bit too soft for salad in the first recipe. Chop them roughly so that they keep their shape and you end up with pieces of tomato in the sauce. Follow the steps below and you'll end up with something I like to call "Syrian Bruschetta." Serve the beans in a shallow dish and pick them up using pita bread as your utensil. Oh, and don't forget to mop up that garlicky tomato sauce at the end!

The second variation is to blend your tomatoes into a smooth sauce before adding them to the pot of beans. Then you add a cup of liquid, like my recipe instructs, and let the ingredients melt into each other. Serve this over rice or any of the grain pilafs in this book and make a gratifying rediscovery of green beans!

stuffed portobello mushrooms

4 portobello mushrooms
2 cups chopped mushrooms (choose your favorite, dried and soaked or fresh)
2 medium onions
2 cups spinach
2 tablespoons extra-virgin olive oil
2 sprigs fresh thyme
¼ cup whole wheat bread crumbs
¼ cup grated Parmigiano Reggiano cheese
1 cup chicken stock, vegetable stock or soaking water from dried mushrooms
Sea salt or Himalayan salt
Black pepper

Preheat oven to 350 degrees Fahrenheit. Peel and dice onions finely. Chop spinach leaves into small pieces. Heat olive oil on medium-high in a large sauté pan. Add onion and thyme, reduce heat to medium-low and sauté until almost translucent, about two minutes. Add chopped mushrooms and continue cooking two minutes. When vegetables are soft, remove thyme sprigs, add bread crumbs, spinach and half the liquid of your choice, and season with salt and pepper. Stir to combine and let sit ten minutes until liquid is absorbed.

Clean portobello mushrooms and remove stems and gills. Sprinkle both sides of mushroom caps with salt and pepper. Divide the stuffing evenly among the mushroom caps, filling generously. Set stuffed mushrooms in a deep casserole dish and pour in the remaining liquid, adding the thyme sprigs. Bake ten minutes in the oven, sprinkle with cheese and return to the oven for five minutes or until cheese browns on top.

FYI

I've explained my cultural obsession with stuffing vegetables, so it won't surprise you that I adored the first stuffed mushroom I tasted in an American restaurant. The hearty flavor of mushrooms and meat was a bit heavy, though, so I took the idea home and played with it until I found the perfect blend: stuff a mushroom with more mushrooms! My favorites for this filling are fresh shiitakes and dried morels because they both stand up well to the prominent flavor of portobellos. When I'd perfected my recipe, I gave it to my mama and friends back home, who all loved the newest addition to our long list of stuffing traditions.

mind, body, soul

the good news

Congratulations, you! I'm so glad you decided to put yourself and your family on the path to the best health possible. Now that you're one of us, there's a secret I'd like to share with you. The purpose of this lifestyle change is to add extra years to your life and make the time you have more fulfilling; it's not to be hot and sexy but to be healthy! However, your partner, friends, family or coworkers may have already noticed that you are sexier! If you commit to living and eating this way, you will see the fabulous side effects of lost weight, amplified energy, positive mood, shiny hair, glowing skin, strong nails and improvement or even healing of many of your current ailments.

Savor your life and enjoy food with gratitude. Incorporate as much of my advice into your day as you can and then work your way past the unhealthy habits that still challenge you. Check your progress at least once a week: What good things have you done for yourself? What did you gain from that? What did you struggle with? Now you have your goal for the next week.

Read on, friend, to reach your full potential health with encouragement and advice on vibrant living that complements the new you.

healthy lifestyle

love your lifestyle

Just Breathe

Healthy lungs need clean, fresh air to exhale toxins out of the body. Deep breathing and outdoor exercise – you know, the huffing and puffing kind-are the most basic ways for our bodies to get oxygen into the bloodstream and out to the internal organs and muscles. Enjoy a walk outdoors as often as you can, ventilate your house well to exchange dust for carbon dioxide and free up your skin from tight-fitting synthetic clothing so it can breathe, too.

Action, Reaction

Again, this is not about numbers like pounds and inches but about years of health and vitality! We're all familiar with popular cardio workouts that beat our behinds into submission, but that's not what I'm talking about here. Brisk walking, jogging or swimming four or more times a week is all it takes to raise your heart rate in a way that benefits the body for years to come. In addition to moderate cardiovascular exercise, stretching, massage, steam and sauna rooms and whirlpool baths positively affect the nervous system, internal organs, blood circulation and detoxification process. Worried about osteoporosis? Resistance exercise (a.k.a. weight training) causes bones to absorb more calcium. Find an activity you enjoy and do it outside whenever possible; that's all it costs you now to avoid pain and doctor's bills later.

Hello, Sunshine

Don't be afraid to sweat! It's one of your body's best defenses against toxic buildup using the largest organ you have: the skin. Although exercise is one way to break a sweat, sun exposure is also a great shield against toxins. But sunbathing at high noon is counterproductive, as many of us now know, and contributes to the formation of skin cancer. Your sunning strategy should be 20 to 30 minutes of direct exposure to the skin (that means no sunscreen except for on the delicate skin of your face and neck) every day during the early morning (from sunrise to 10 a.m.) or late afternoon (4 p.m. to sunset). Combine it with outdoor exercise and you've just earned your daily value of vitamin D and protected your body from disease. Now you're multitasking.

Optimal Aqua

You are what you drink – about 70 percent of the body is water, so consuming clean water with the right pH should be a top priority. Drinking water is important for elimination of toxins, blood flow, cellular function, digestion, relieving constipation, suppressing appetite and metabolizing stored fat.

I'll give you some good options, starting with what the experts recognize as the best and following with other efficient solutions for keeping your family hydrated at home.

Distilled – Considering all the pollution that makes its way into our food, it shouldn't surprise you that the water in our earth has picked up those same herbicides and pesticides we try to avoid. For this reason, experts agree that distilling is the only sure way to get pure drinking water. However, during the process of distilling, the molecules of our H2O become unstructured and therefore less usable to the body. The easiest way to restructure water after distilling is to add a pinch of salt per gallon of water and leave the water in the moonlight overnight. The next morning, you have not only clean water but a structure the body can absorb and put to good use.

Spring – This is the most readily available option at your grocery store, but not all spring water is equal. Make sure you're getting the cleanest water by purchasing brands known for their purity, such as Evian, Fuji and Panna (although this is not an exhaustive list, and with a little research, you can probably find several others worth drinking). Last and most important, buy your water bottled in glass. I can't stress how many studies have proved that plastic containers leak manufacturing chemicals into their contents. If you must buy plastic, turn the bottle over and look at the triangular recycling symbol at the bottom. The number you see should be 1, 2, 4 or 5, or it can even be a corn-based plastic. Many health food stores now carry reusable water bottles made with PLA (corn-based plastic). Just watch out for numbers 3, 6 and 7, as they are most guilty of leaching harmful chemicals into contents, especially when heated or reused.

Filter – A water filtration system is a relatively inexpensive option, especially for those who have tap water that has been deemed safe by the EPA*. You can purchase systems that filter water for the whole house or smaller systems that fit right onto your kitchen faucet. This can be a good solution for those who want to fill their own bottles, prefer not to use manufactured plastics or just don't want the expense of store-bought water.

*To see if your local water source is within the Environmental Protection Agency's guidelines for drinkable water, visit the EPA's online search engine, find your state and county and select your community water system from the list. All violations are listed in italics.

http://www.epa.gov/enviro/html/sdwis/sdwis_ov.html

Index

Works Consulted

cookware

Aronson, Tara. "A Healthy Fridge." Housekeeping channel. The Housekeeping Channel LLC, 2 December 2004. Web. < http://www.housekeepingchannel.com/a_153-A_ Healthy_Fridge>.

Blunt, Richard. "The healthy kitchen: Good spoons, good knives, good food." Backwoods Home Magazine. Backwoods Home Magazine, 1998. Web. <http://www. backwoodshome.com/articles2/blunt102.html>.

Esko, Edward. "Energy." Kushi Institute. Kushi Institute, December 1993. Web. <http://www. kushiinstitute.org/html/articles.html#energy>.

"FAQ: Should I buy pre-seasoned cast iron cookware?" Healthy Child Healthy World. Healthy Child Healthy World, 2011. Web. <http://healthychild.org/live-healthy/faq/ cookware_bakeware-cast_iron#ixzz12poviam1>.

"The Healthy Fridge." Open the Door to a Healthy Heart. Open the Door to a Healthy Heart, 2009. Web <http://www.healthyfridge.org/questions.html>.

"How to Brew Tea." Tea Party Guide. The Tea Party Guide, 2011. Web. <http://www.tea-party-guide.com/brew-tea.html>.

"Knife Materials." Chef Depot. Chef Depot Inc., 2011. Web <http://www.chefdepot.net/ knifematerials.htm>.

Maker, Melissa. "Cleaning Green." Naturally Savvy. Healthy Shopper, 2010. Web <http:// www.naturallysavvy.com/cleaning-green>.

Mercola, Dr. Joseph. "Ceramic Teaware." Mercola.com. Dr. Joseph Mercola, 2011. Web. <http://cookware.mercola.com/ceramic-teaware.aspx>.

Richards, Birgit. "Your life and plastics." Greenearth feng shui. Greenearth feng shui, 2011. Web. <http://www.greenearth-fengshui.com.au/healthy-homes>.

Rosa, Gabriela. "Dangerous vs. Safe Cookware and Utensils (PART 2)." Natural Fertility Breakthrough. Natural Fertility and Health Solutions, 13 August 2009. Web. <http:// naturalfertilitybreakthrough.com/articles/dangerous-vs-safe-cookware-and-utensils-part-2/>.

Utendorf, Heather. "Healthy Kitchen." AboutMyPlanet. AboutMyPlanet, 20 March 2008. Web . <http://www.aboutmyplanet.com/daily-green-tips/healthy-kitchen>.

Yates, Tom F. "Easiest Tips in Cleaning Your Kitchen Utensils." Ezine @rticles. Ezine Articles.com, 12 March 2010. Web. <http://ezinearticles.com/?Easiest-Tips-in-Cleaning-Your-Kitchen-Utensils&id=3920770>.

pantry

Abreo, Victoria. "Sea Salt vs Table Salt." Bella Online. Victoria Abreo, 2011. Web. <http:// www.bellaonline.com/articles/art2440.asp>.

Accad, Joumana. "Strawberry and Raspberry jam with agar-agar in 10 minutes." Taste of Beirut. taste of beirut, 9 February 2011.

"Amaranth." Alfalfa House. Alfalfa House, 2011. Web. <http://www.alfalfahouse.org/html/ PRODUCTS/SPECIFIC_PRODUCTS/amaranth.htm>.

Andoh, Elizabeth. Washoku: recipes from the Japanese home kitchen. Berkeley: Ten Speed Press, 2005. Print.

Beck, Leslie. "Kamut – August 2008's Featured Food." Leslie Beck, RD. Leslie Beck, August 2008. Web. <http://www.lesliebeck.com/ingredient_index.php?featured_food=100>.

Bette, Sue. "Quest for the Best Canned Tuna." feel good eats. WordPress, 4 August 2008. Web. <http://www.feelgoodeats.com/whole-foods-information/quest-for-the-best-canned-tuna.html>.

Biali, Dr. Susan. "How Sweet It Is – A Guide to Natural Sweeteners." Dr. Susan Biali, M.D. Susan Biali, . Web. <http://www.susanbiali.com/health-and-nutrition/how-sweet-it-is-a-guide-to-natural-sweeteners.html>.

"Black Pepper." The world's healthiest foods. The George Mateljan Foundation, 2011. Web. <http://www.whfoods.com/genpage.php?tname=foodspice&dbid=74>.

Blaylock, Russell L. Exitotoxins: the Taste that Kills. Santa Fe: Health Press, 1997. Print.

Boyes, Roger. "Death for hire." The Times. Times Newspapers Ltd., 29 March 2008. Web. <http://www.timesonline.co.uk/tol/news/world/europe/article3641866.ece>.

"Choosing and cooking whole grains." Natural Markets. PCC Natural Markets, 2011. Web. <http://www.pccnaturalmarkets.com/guides/tips_grains.html>.

"Choosing and cooking with beans." Natural Markets. PCC Natural Markets, 2011. Web. <http://www.pccnaturalmarkets.com/guides/tips_beans.html>.

"Choosing and preparing rice." Natural Markets. PCC Natural Markets, 2011. Web. <http://www.pccnaturalmarkets.com/guides/tips_rice.html>.

"Choosing the right cooking oil." PCC Natural Markets. PCC Natural Markets, 2011. Web. <http://www.pccnaturalmarkets.com/guides/tips_cooking_oils.html>.

"Corn Grain." What's on my food? Pesticide Action Network North America, 2008. Web. <http://www.whatsonmyfood.org/food.jsp?food=CO>.

Cox, Jeff. The Organic Food Shopper's Guide. Hoboken: John Wiley & Sons, Inc., 2008. Print.

Dufty, William. "Refined Sugar – The Sweetest poison of All… ." Global Healing Center. Global Healing Center, 2011. Web. <http://www.globalhealingcenter.com/refined-sugar-the-sweetest-poison-of-all.html>.

Editors of Easy Home Cooking Magazine. "Food Storage Tips: How to Store Vinegar." TLC. Discovery Communications LLC, 2011. Web. <http://recipes.howstuffworks.com/tools-and-techniques/food-storage-tips3.htm>.

Fife, Bruce. The Coconut Oil Miracle. New York: Avery, 2004. Print.

Food Network Kitchens. "Kosher vs. table vs. sea salts." food network.com. Television Food Network G.P., 2011.

Giese, Paula. "MAHNOOMIN -- Wild Rice, Sacred Gift -- the Story." Native Recipes. Paula Giese, 6 June 1997. Web. <http://www.kstrom.net/isk/food/r_wild.html>.

Grace, Divine. "How To Use Sucanat In Food." Health Recipes.com. WordPress, 30 April 2010. Web. <http://healthrecipes.com/health_sucanat.htm>.

"Healthy diet 'cuts dementia risk'." BBC News. BBC, 13 November 2007. Web. <http://news.bbc.co.uk/2/hi/health/7092292.stm>.

Henneman, Alice. "Add a little SPICE (& HERBS) to Your Life!" University of Nebraska-Lincoln. University of Nebraska, 2011. Web <http://lancaster.unl.edu/food/spiceherbshandout-color.pdf%20>.

"Honey." The world's healthiest foods. The George Mateljan Foundation, 2011. Web. <http://www.whfoods.com/genpage.php?tname=foodspice&dbid=96>.

"iodine." The world's healthiest foods. The George Mateljan Foundation, 2011. Web. <http://www.whfoods.com/genpage.php?tname=nutrient&dbid=69#factorswhichaffect>.

Jaworski, Stephanie. "Vanilla." Joy of Baking.com. iFood Media LLC, 2011. Web. <http://www.joyofbaking.com/Vanilla.html>.

Kohler, John. "The Truth about Agave Syrup: Not as Healthy as You May Think." Living and Raw Foods. Living-Foods.com, 2008. Web. <http://www.living-foods.com/articles/agave.html>.

"Making Mitoku Brown Rice Vinegar." Mitoku. Mitoku Company, Ltd., 2011. Web. <http://www.mitoku.com/products/ricevinegar/making_vinegar.html>.

Mercola, Dr. Joseph. "The 13 Amazing Health Benefits of Himalayan Crystal Salt, the Purest Salt on Earth." Mercola.com. Dr. Joseph Mercola, 2011. Web. <http://products.mercola.com/himalayan-salt/>.

Messina, Virginia. "The Fatty Acids." VeganHealth.org. VeganHealth.org, 2011. Web. <http://www.veganhealth.org/articles/fattyacids>.

Mikkelson, Barbara. "Oil of Olé." Snopes.com. Urban Legends Reference Pages, 30 December 2005. Web. <http://www.snopes.com/medical/toxins/canola.asp>.

Myers, Robert L. and Meinke, Louis J. "Buckwheat: A Multi-Purpose, Short-Season Alternative." University of Missouri Extension. University of Missouri Extension, April 1994. Web. <http://extension.missouri.edu/publications/DisplayPub.aspx?P=G4306>.

Nielsen, Per H. "Kartoffelmel production." LCA Food Database. The Institute for Product development, February 2004. Web <http://www.lcafood.dk/processes/industry/potatoflourproduction.htm>.

"Olive Oil Quality." Info Comm. UNCTAD.org, 1996. Web. <http://www.unctad.org/infocomm/anglais/olive/quality.htm>.

Ostrander, Chrys. "Some Answers About Pectin." The Future is Organic. thefutureisorganic.net, 2011. Web. <http://www.thefutureisorganic.net/pectin.htm>.

Perryman, Shirley. "Spice up your diet and do your body good." Today @ Colorado State. Colorado State University, 20 August 2010. Web. <http://www.today.colostate.edu/story.aspx?id=4296>.

"Quinoa." Alfalfa House. Alfalfa House, 2011. Web. <http://www.alfalfahouse.org/html/PRODUCTS/SPECIFIC_PRODUCTS/quinoa.htm>.

Reinagel, Monica. "What Kind of Salt is Healthiest?" Quick and Dirty Tips. Macmillan Holdings, LLC, 1 June 2010. Web. <http://nutritiondiva.quickanddirtytips.com/what-kind-of-salt-is-healthiest.aspx>.

Ruhlman, Michael. "Salt. Is It Good or Bad?" Michael Ruhlman. Ruhlman Enterprises, 21 January 2010. Web. <http://ruhlman.com/2010/01/salt-is-it-good-or-bad/>.

Russell, Robin L. "Millet Fact Sheet." Recipes For Natural Health. Robin L. Russell, 2001. Web. <http://www.recipenet.org/health/articles/millet.htm>.

Shulman, Martha Rose. "An Elegant Gruel: Polenta." The New York Times. The New York Times Company, 8 June 2009. Web. <http://www.nytimes.com/2009/06/08/health/nutrition/08recipehealth.html?ref=polenta>.

Sideman, Eva. "How sugar is made." Made How. Advameg, Inc., 2011. Web. <http://www.madehow.com/Volume-1/Sugar.html>.

"Spelt." The world's healthiest foods. The George Mateljan Foundation, 2011. Web. <http://www.whfoods.com/genpage.php?tname=foodspice&dbid=143>.

"Thickeners and Vegetable Gums." Food Additives. food-additives, 2011. Web. <http://www.foodadditivesworld.com/thickeners-and-vegetable-gums.html>.

USDA Organic Seal and Radura Symbol images provided by U.S. Department of Agriculture. <http://www.flickr.com/photos/usdagov/6350829995/> <http://www.fsis.usda.gov/images/radura300.jpg>

"What are the best fish to buy?" The world's healthiest foods. The George Mateljan Foundation, 2011. Web. <http://www.whfoods.com/genpage.php?tname=george&dbid=105>.

"White balsamic vinegar." Baker & Olive. Baker & Olive, 2011. Web. <http://bakerandolive.com/shop/white-balsamic-vinegar/>.

shopping

Behrenbeck, Dr. Thomas. "High cholesterol." Mayo Clinic. Mayo Foundation for Medical Education and Research, 22 Dec. 2009. Web. <http://www.mayoclinic.com/health/cholesterol/HQ00608>.

Bennett, Beverly Lynn. "Plant-Based Calcium: Sources and Absorbability." Veg Kitchen. Amberwood Press, Inc., 2 Jan. 2008. Web. <http://www.vegkitchen.com/nutrition/calcium/>.

Bergeson, Laine. "Why Whole Milk is the Healthiest Choice." Experience Life. Life Time Fitness, Inc., 28 Jan. 2008. Web. <http://blogs.experiencelifemag.com/signs-of-life/2009/01/why-whole-milk-is-the-healthiest-choice.html>.

Blaisdell, Shannon. "An Illustrated Guide to Beef Roasts." Cooks Illustrated. Web. America's Test Kitchen, November 2002. <http://www.cooksillustrated.com/images/document/howto/ND02_BeefRoasts.pdf>.

Bouchard, Maryse F., et al. "Attention-Deficit/Hyperactivity Disorder and Urinary Metabolites of Organophosphate Pesticides." Pediatrics. American Academy of Pediatrics, 23 February 2010. Web. <http://pediatrics.aappublications.org/content/early/2010/05/17/peds.2009-3058.abstract>.

Bradley, Jeanette. "Shellfish Allergy: What You Need To Know." About.com. About.com, 4 June 2011. Web. <http://foodallergies.about.com/od/seafoodallergies/p/shellfish.htm>.

Coates, Amy. "The Low Down on Margarine and Fats." total wellness consulting. total wellness consulting, 18 Dec. 2007. Web. <http://www.totalwellnessconsulting.ca/margarine.htm>.

Conis, Elena. "Sprouted-grain breads: the facts." Los Angeles Times. Los Angeles Times, 12 Oct. 2009. Web. <http://articles.latimes.com/2009/oct/12/health/he-nutrition12>.

DiBella, Lorraine. "Is Our Seafood Safe to Eat?" North Carolina State University. NC State University, 2011. Web. <http://www.ces.ncsu.edu/depts/foodsci/ext/pubs/Is%20our%20seafood%20safe%20to%20eat.pdf>.

"Ethylene Gas." Mindfully.org. Mindfully.org, 2011. Web. <http://www.mindfully.org/Plastic/Ethylene-Gas.htm>.

Foran, Stacy E., et al. "Measurement of Mercury Levels in Concentrated Over-the-Counter Fish Oil Preparations." Archives of Pathology and Laboratory Medicine 127 (2003): 1603-1605. Archives of Pathology.org. Web. 11 Feb. 2011.

Greer, Betty. "A Guide to Buying Fresh Fruits & Vegetables." Tennessee State University Extension. Tennessee State University, 2011. Web. <https://utextension.tennessee.edu/publications/Documents/SP527.pdf>.

Griesbauer, Laura. "Methylmercury Contamination in Fish and Shellfish." ProQuest. CSA, February 2007. Web. <http://www.csa.com/discoveryguides/mercury/review4.php>.

Hackett, Jolinda. "Who are some famous vegetarians?" About.com. About.com, 2011. Web. <http://vegetarian.about.com/od/vegetarianlifestyle/f/famousveg.htm>.

"How Much Calcium is in That?" fitsugar. Sugar Inc., 21 March 2007. Web. <http://www.fitsugar.com/How-Much-Calcium-182622>.

"How Much Meat We Eat." PBS.org. WGBH educational foundation, 2011. Web. <http://www.pbs.org/wgbh/pages/frontline/shows/meat/safe/howmuch.html>.

Knutson, Patty. "Vegan Baking Tips, Techniques and Recipes." Vegan Coach. VeganCoach.com, 2011. Web. <http://www.vegancoach.com/vegan-baking.html>.

Kustes, Scott. "Nutrition in Milk And Milk Substitutes." Naked Food Cooking. Naked Food Cooking, 2011. Web. <http://www.nakedfoodcooking.com/nutrition-milk-milk-substitutes/>.

Larsen, Hans R. "Fish oils and mercury." oilofpisces.com Database. Hans R. Larsen, 2011. Web. <http://www.oilofpisces.com/mercury.html>.

Mother Earth News Editors. "How to Make Sprouted Grain Bread." Mother Earth News. Ogden Publications Inc., January 1984. Web. <http://www.motherearthnews.com/real-food/essene-bread-sprouted-grain.aspx>.

"Nutrition Comparison of Shellfish." CNN Interactive. Cable News Network, 2000. Web. <http://www.cnn.com/FOOD/resources/food.for.thought/meat/seafood/compare.shellfish.html>.

"Organic Farming Practices: Postharvest Handling." University of California. University of California, 2011. Web. <http://vric.ucdavis.edu/pdf/postharvest_organic_handling.pdf>.

"Organic foods in relation to nutrition and health key facts." Medical News Today. MediLexicon International Ltd, 11 July 2004. Web. <http://www.medicalnewstoday.com/releases/10587.php>.

Perry, Marge. "A Milk Primer." Cooking Light. Time Inc. Lifestyle Group, 2011. Web. <http://www.cookinglight.com/eating-smart/nutrition-101/a-milk-primer-00400000001455/>.

Phillips, Sarah. "Bread 101 – Ingredients." baking 911. baking911.com, 2008. Web. <http://www.baking911.com/bread/101_ingredients.htm#Ingredients>.

Pugliese, Gerald. "Vegetable-Based Nitrates Can Help Preserve Pork, Organically." Organic authority. Organic Authority LLC, 19 November 2009. Web. <http://www.

organicauthority.com/blog/organic/vegetable-based-nitrates-can-help-preserve-pork-organically/>.

"A Review of Human Carcinogens." International Agency for Research on Cancer. IARC, 17 May 2011. Web. <http://monographs.iarc.fr/ENG/Classification/ClassificationsAlphaOrder.pdf>.

Savell, Jeff. "Metmyoglobin formation in ground beef." Meat Science at Texas A&M. Texas A&M University, 2011. Web. <http://meat.tamu.edu/metmyoglobin.html>.

"Seafood Allergy." Auckland Allergy Clinic. Auckland Allergy Clinic, Feb. 2003. Web. <http://www.allergyclinic.co.nz/guides/51.html>.

"Seasonal Produce Guide." Your Produce. Majon International, 2011. Web. <http://www.yourproduce.com/>.

Watson, Molly. "Guide to Seasonal Fruits & Vegetables." About.com. About.com, 2011. Web. <http://localfoods.about.com/od/finduselocalfoods/a/natlseason.htm>.

Weingarten, Hemi. "Five Bread Ingredients to Avoid." Fooducate Blog. Fooducate, 4 Nov. 2010. Web. <http://www.fooducate.com/blog/2010/11/04/five-bread-ingredients-to-avoid-miniseries-part-4/>.

Wittenberg, Margaret M. "What to Look for on a Bread Ingredients Label." NEW GOOD FOOD. NEW GOOD FOOD, 2011. Web. <http://www.newgoodfood.com/recipes/breadlabel.html>.

"Types of Bread." Bake Info. Baking Industry Research Trust, 2011. Web. <http://www.bakeinfo.co.nz/Facts/Bread-making/Types-of-bread>.

mind, body, soul

Campbell, Dr. Colin T. and Thomas M. Campbell II. The China Study. Dallas: BenBella Books, Inc., 2006. Print.

Clement, Dr. Brian R. Hippocrates Health Program - A Proven Guide to Healthful Living. West Palm Beach: Hippocrates Books, 1989. Print.

Clement, Dr. Brian R. Supplements Exposed. Franklin Lakes: Career Press, 2010. Print.

"Safe Drinking Water Information System – Search." EPA. United States Environmental Protection Agency, 2011. Web. <http://www.epa.gov/enviro/facts/sdwis/search.html>.

About the Author

Yara is an ordinary woman with an extraordinary appetite for knowledge about healthy living. She decided to dig deep into the facts of nutrition and health to learn how every bite would affect her and her loved ones. As a result, she created an ideal lifestyle centered on natural nourishment with real flavor. The principles are simple: savor the things you love and keep everything in proportion to be healthy and happy.

When she arrived in the United States as a young woman, Yara brought a deep appreciation for her Syrian cultural cuisine that she gained as an apprentice to one of the top chefs in Damascus. She combined traditional flavors with new healthy techniques to reinvent her family recipes. Most importantly, Yara brings a love of fresh, flavorful ingredients and enthusiasm to the kitchen that makes every meal memorable.

A former business student, model, esthetician and owner of a high-end clothing boutique, Yara is passionate about sharing her experiences and offering women advice for making their bodies beautiful from the inside out. She's also an avid traveler with expertise in planning luxury escapes to outstanding destinations. Now Yara has collected her unique approaches to healthy cooking, beauty, style, wedding and event planning and travel online. Visit **www.YarasWay.com** to explore this exciting women's lifestyle guide.